Dear Lily

~THE · WILLIAM · ALFRED · VIOLETT HOUSE · CIRCA · 1850 ·
· FOURTH & PRYTANNIA · ST · NEW · ORLEANS ·

Dear Lily

A LOVE STORY

by Malcolm W. Greenough, Jr.

YANKEE BOOKS

A division of Yankee Publishing Incorporated
Dublin, New Hampshire

Designed by Jill Shaffer.
Frontispiece courtesy of Ellen Violett.

Yankee Publishing Incorporated
Dublin, New Hampshire 03444
First Edition
Second Printing, 1987
Copyright 1987 by Malcolm W. Greenough, Jr.

Library of Congress Cataloging-in-Publication Data

Greenough, Malcolm W., 1926-
Dear Lily.

1. Violett, Lily, 1854-1937 — Fiction. 2. New
Orleans (La.) — History — Fiction. I. Violett, Lily,
1854-1937. II. Title.
PS3557.R3963D4   1987   813'54   87–2124
ISBN 0-89909-136-9

Acknowledgements

Many people have helped me with this book. My wife, Catherine, gave me a lot of much needed moral support and many helpful ideas, but wisely wouldn't read the work until it had been accepted for publication. I especially want to thank my agent, Llewellyn Howland III, whose enthusiasm and efforts made the book's publication a reality.

Clarissa Silitch, the acquiring editor for Yankee Books, contributed many hours of her considerable editing skills to polish and refine the story without altering it in any substantive way.

Stanton Frazar, former Director of the Historic New Orleans Collection, introduced me to that fine organization, and to Dr. Patricia B. Schmit, head of its Publication Department, and other members of the staff, who gave much valuable advice on the book's historical accuracy.

To all of these, and the many others who contributed to this book, my heartfelt thanks.

M.W.G., Jr.

Introduction

After my mother died in 1966, I found in her house, now my own, a mass of old documents and other materials relating to the Violett family of New Orleans, the Whelen family of Philadelphia, and the Greenough family of Boston. Because neither of my parents had ever mentioned the existence of this material, nor told me anything about these families, from whom I am descended, it took me a great deal of time and effort to assemble it all into a coherent whole. The results inspired this book.

The framework of this account is a series of letters from my great great aunt Lily Violett to her great nephew, my father, Malcolm Whelen Greenough. Included in the story are many of the actual letters to and from the central characters, portions of their diaries and Aunt Lily's memoirs, old newspaper clippings, items from scrapbooks, and old family photographs. Other letters are based on facts derived from family records and outside sources. Certain liberties have been taken in the name of romance, but otherwise the account is as historically accurate as possible.

The many personal possessions of the Violett, Whelen, and Greenough families that are here in the house and that I have been able to identify as theirs — clothing, books, paintings, photographs, furniture, china, and silverware — have been of great assistance to me. They speak of the lives of their owners almost as eloquently as the written word. Also most revealing are two of the family houses, in Boston and Philadelphia, that still exist in much their original condition.

Reconstructing the lives of these previously unknown ancestors has been a wonderful experience for me. I hope that the reader will share my pleasure in stepping through this doorway to the past.

Malcolm W. Greenough, Jr.
Prides Crossing, Mass.
September, 1986

Chapter 1

7 Gloucester Street
Boston
Massachusetts

June 17, 1925

Dear Mally,

   I am sitting at the writing desk in your room looking out the window at the cars going up and down Gloucester Street and listening to the Gramophone music being played in the parlor downstairs by some of the young people that your grandfather asked back after the reception. The words were, "I wanna be loved by you, just you . . ." or something like that. They seem strange to your great aunt's seventy-one year old ears and set me thinking about the past and the kind of music I used to hear through my windows back in New Orleans in the 1850's when I was just a little girl. What a lot has happened between then and now!

   I'm tired to a frazzle from your wedding, but I wouldn't have missed it for the world. Kathleen is a darling girl, so pretty and so bright! I know you're both going to be very happy. You know how much I care for you and how I suffered for you and with you through all the unhappiness of your childhood. You had to endure so much! It is so wonderful to see you rewarded now with such a lovely wife and a bright, rich future. It makes me feel that something that has been holding me in all these years has suddenly loosened its grip — that I can look at my past and my future (whatever I have left) with a peace and satisfaction that I never felt before.

9

Now I have this great desire to tell you about what I have seen and heard during my life. I say "seen" because I haven't "done" very much, but oh what I've seen and heard. And you should know about all the people in the families that you came from — about their troubles and triumphs, and especially about the mother and father you never knew. And I can tell you. I was there and lived through it all. I am one of the few survivors.

I'll be going to New York the day after tomorrow to stay with brother Atwood for the summer in the Adirondacks. You know he keeps a camp up there now and has all the children and grandchildren up whenever he can. It will be a perfect place for me to start writing my story. It's so strange. I never thought I even wanted to think about all those difficult years, but now I can't wait to get them on paper. Despite the pain, they were filled with events that I think will interest you.

Dearest Mally, you have made everything worthwhile for me. I am so very, very happy for you and I thank you for all the love and consideration you have given me over the years when I needed it so badly. Have a wonderful honeymoon in Europe! Give my love to Kathleen. With deepest affection and love,

Aunt Lily

Camp Laurel
Tupper Lake
New York

July 9, 1925

Dear Mally,

After I finished my letter to you from Boston in June I looked at it and thought, Did I really write that? I can't believe I can possibly be undertaking to relive all those years. I'd better tear it up and start again.

While I thought about it I was addressing the envelope:

Malcolm Whelen Greenough
S.S. Olympia, White Star Line
Pier 59, New York City, N.Y.

And, still wondering whether to send it, I wrote my home address on the back:

Miss Lily Violett
3915 St. Charles Avenue
New Orleans, La.

Then, not giving myself time to reconsider, I stuffed the letter in the envelope, licked and sealed the flap — I would do it.

Well, I promised you the family history, so here goes. I've never tried to do anything like this before and I don't have any plan about it, so I might as well begin at the beginning as they say, or at least as close to it as I can remember. Unlike many people, I don't have a very complete memory for my early childhood. Only a few small incidents loom above the fog that shrouds those years. Indeed the memory that I had in Boston of the following experience sparked this enterprise.

As when I wrote you from Boston a month ago, it was early summer and late afternoon. New Orleans was drowsy with the heat, waiting expectantly for an evening breeze to add some degree of coolness. Ordinarily, we would have been up river at the Farm by this time, getting ready for our annual trip north to avoid the Fever, but some occasion had brought us to town for a week. I was five years old, so it must have been 1859 — just two short years before the start of the war that was to destroy our lives as a New Orleans family.

I was playing on the gallery that opened off the bedrooms on the second floor of our house at the corner of Prytania and Fourth Streets with my older sister Ella who was nine, and baby Mignonette. Little Edwin, who was three, was sick, and my mother had him with her in the sewing room. It was about five o'clock; I was bored and a bit annoyed with Ella for hogging baby sister Minnie's attention, so I walked down to the end of the gallery and leaned on the railing to look out for men on horses, or people in carriages going up and down Fourth Street. Maybe it is because it was so long ago, but it seemed as though the heat and the dust muffled all sounds. The clatter of pots and pans in the kitchen just two floors below seemed very remote, and horses' hooves struck silently on the dusty street.

As the sun made it too bright to look to the southwest, I was gazing out in the other direction when far up Fourth Street I saw a strange-looking man coming our way. He was so far away at first and the light was so bad that it was hard to see him clearly, but as he got closer I saw that he was dressed in a homespun tunic and his feet were bound in rags. A tangled, ropy mass of dirty white hair hung over his shoulders and halfway down his back. A similar beard covered his chest and swung heavily from side to side as he walked.

Most astonishing of all, he was carrying a large scythe over one shoulder, balancing it with one skinny hand draped loosely over the shaft. As he got closer still, I could see that his skin was almost white, not burned or tanned at all, and his eyes were rheumy and red rimmed. He was a most unpleasant sight, and, although my eyes were glued to him in horrified fascination, I was aware that other people on the street were giving him a wide berth. And then, horror of horrors, as he passed below me he looked up and met my eyes for one electrifying moment. It still brings me a shudder when I think of it.

Then he was gone around the corner and, as though he had never existed, the street resumed its ordinarily placid state. I was called to supper, and the memory of this bizarre event vanished for the moment. Later though, I often wondered about it. It was not that I had never seen raggedy people before — I saw plenty in the countryside above the city — but our house in New Orleans was in a very fashionable district, and such people had no business to take them there. And he was so white he didn't look like a farmer at all. I told Mama about it, but she didn't pay much attention, nor did Ella, so I told baby Minnie. She agreed that it was very singular indeed.

It was our names that were the cause of the second childhood incident that has remained with me over the years. My oldest sister was called Ella but her real name was Heliotrope, mine is Lily and baby's name was Mignonette. Of course our surname was Violett and even my oldest brother Atwood was known as "Wood" Violett.

One day when I was six, the whole family was attending some social affair at a neighbor's house, I forget exactly whose, and I was standing alone by the door to a parlor. A lovely young woman, a real

Southern Belle in all her finery, approached me and said, "My, you're a pretty little thing. What's your name?" Craning my neck back to look up at her, I replied, "Lily Violett, Ma'am," and she said, "Oh! You're one of the floral Violetts!" I was so surprised! I had never heard that reference to us before. I really liked the idea that we were all joined in such a nice way.

Let me interrupt my story here to tell you a little about the family and our home in New Orleans. Family history disappears so quickly if no one writes it down. You probably won't be too interested now, but when you get older you will be.

My mother, your great grandmother, was born Penelope Oldham in 1825 at Louisville, Kentucky, the youngest daughter of Captain Richard Oldham and Eliza Martin Oldham. Grandma Oldham was the daughter of her future husband's commanding officer, Major Thomas Martin. She was born in 1793 when her father was commandant of the Newport Barracks in Kentucky, just across the Ohio River from Cincinnati. She used to tell us wonderful stories about the old days: how her father fought as a cadet and then a lieutenant under General George Washington at Brandywine Creek and how he was captured at the battle of Germantown because the fog was so thick that his company advanced right into the enemy camp, and when the fog suddenly lifted, there they were — surrounded by the British.

After the War of Independence her father stayed in the army, as did his brother William, and they had many adventures serving at Army forts along the western frontier. By the Treaty of Paris of 1783 the British were supposed to abandon their forts in the Northwest, but they didn't, and also provided the Indian Nations with weapons and incited them to raid the settlers in Ohio and Kentucky. America was young and weak and ripe to be taken over by any or all of the European powers, so fighting was pretty constant on the western frontier. Especially exciting to us children was the story of how our mother's great uncle William Oldham got killed in the skirmish known as "St. Clair's Defeat" near Fort Recovery, Ohio, in the Indian Wars of 1791. It was said that he was killed in hand to hand combat by Tecumseh, the great Shawnee Chief.

When Grandma Oldham's father's regiment was transferred to New Orleans in 1808, all the men and the officers' families went by flatboat down the Ohio and Mississippi Rivers, there being no steamboats at that time. These "flatboats" were actually huge rafts up to eighty feet long made of logs fastened together with rope and cross pieces, with a real log cabin complete with stone fireplace built on top. The cabin not only provided shelter from the elements, but also offered protection from Indian attack, which was still very common west of the Allegheny Mountains (although no attack would be made against the regiment unless one of the rafts became separated from the rest by some misfortune).

The trip took about six weeks, and Grandma Oldham, who was fifteen at the time, said it was one of the most pleasant and interesting experiences of her life. When a settlement was near at nightfall, the rafts would tie up along the bank and all the children were allowed to go ashore to play. The settlement families would come down to the riverbank to sell the troops fresh milk, eggs and vegetables, their shy children would be coaxed to play, and the parents to stay and share the evening meal. There was singing, exchange of gossip and recipes by the women, and talk of politics and Indian skirmishes by the men as they smoked their pipes in groups around the camp fires.

Still, for the most part, the country around the river was wild and empty of white settlers then, though there were many Indians to be seen along the shore or in canoes on the river. Back from the shore, rising columns of smoke marked the sites of many encampments. It's hard to believe it could all change so much in a short hundred years.

Day after day the rafts (or flatboats) drifted downstream, poling around obstructions and steering with the great sweeps lashed to the stern. All the boats were handled by professional river men known as "Kaintucks," a corruption of the name of the state from which so many of them came. They were rough, colorful men dressed in homespun clothes and Indian-made moccasin boots, the leather thongs crisscrossed around their calves. Each wore a large "Bowie" knife in his belt that they used for everything from chopping wood to picking their teeth. They swore and spat tobacco juice and seemed always on the verge of violence, but their boss told Grandma, whom he saw eyeing them apprehensively, that she had nothing to fear as long as they were on the river. "They're savin' up for N'Orleans," he said and laughed. "They're savin' up."

Grandma would describe the times when the river opened wide, as much as two miles from shore to shore, and the cluster of rafts and boats would drift along all through the night, each with a tall pole topped with a lantern that added light to the scene only when the moon passed behind a cloud. Otherwise it seemed as bright as day. Only the river itself was dark. I remember her saying, "It was as if we were fixed in place on a gigantic flat black snake undulating over the land. At night you could actually feel the tremendous weight, the immensity of the river and the uncomprehendable 'bigness' of the land around it. It was such a powerful feeling, like nothing else I have ever experienced."

I have always had a great love for houses. To me they tell so much about the people that built them and the way of life that the house was designed to provide. Nowhere could I have found houses with more to tell than in New Orleans, a city that contained within its borders such diverse types as the huge pillared plantation mansions in the Garden District and the narrow European-looking town houses lavishly embellished with wrought or cast iron balconies and fences in the French Quarter.

The raised cottage, another popular style, with its "first" floor some six feet above ground level and ground floor below, was really a one-story building with the living area raised up to better catch any cooling breezes during the baking hot summer months. The so-called ground floor wasn't used for much of anything but storage.

Plantation mansions, known later as "Creole Classic," combined Greek Revival with the practicality of a pitched roof that extended as much as twenty feet beyond the walls of the house — sometimes on all sides. With their elegant columns soaring from the ground level piazza forty feet or more to the cornice of the roof, I have always thought them to be the loveliest example of domestic architecture ever created. As a little girl I used to dream about one day becoming the mistress of such a house.

Our house on Prytania Street in the Garden District was an amalgamation of many styles — a successful one according to all who knew it. Built about 1850 on three lots, it combined the raised cottage with the heavy cast iron balconies of the Vieux Carré and the interior room layout of the smaller plantation houses. It had almost an acre of land around it, and the house was on the southwest corner, its walls about twenty-five feet from the cast iron fence that ran around the two street sides of the property. Along the other two sides ran a stuccoed brick wall, eight feet high and verdigrised to mottled patches of greens and blues that so blended with the oleander and Spanish Dagger planted in front of it that it was all but invisible. To the eye, the property had no rearward enclosure except trees and bushes.

In the northeast corner was the stable and next to it a low, one-story house for the stableboys and such.

I'll take you on a tour of the house as though we had just arrived at the front gate, which was set right in the corner where the two streets meet.

We enter through the gate and proceed up the flagstone path to the steps that take us up to the front door. They run parallel to the house and have a cast iron railing of the same design as that of the railings on the western and eastern ends of the house enclosing the galleries there. The house is built of yellow brick with protruding bands of brick at the ground level, the first and second floor levels, and a final band running around the house just under the eaves. Yellow brick sills and headers protrude from the side of the house under and over each window. The brick between these bands and the windows and doors is stuccoed in an off-white plaster. (Do you know I'm doing this from memory! I know that house so well I don't even have to look at its picture.)

The front door opens onto a hall about twelve feet wide. On the left is the parlor, a large room about twenty by thirty-two feet, with four window-doors opening onto the gallery. On the right is the smaller dining room with a black marble-fronted fireplace. Before you is the loveliest front hall staircase in all New Orleans (in my opinion anyway). The treads narrow toward the right-hand wall as it ascends, giving the railing on the left a delicate inward curve rising almost to the vertical as it swoops around to the left on its way to the second floor. Behind the stairs a door opens out onto a stone stairway leading to the grounds behind the house. It is of the type the Bermudians call a "welcoming arms" stairway, narrowing from the broad base to the smaller top step.

Another interior door next to the back door leads off to the right to the back hall that goes past the dining room and, beyond that, Papa's study, both on the right. This hall also gives access to the back stairs and an ell off to the left that contains the kitchen, pantry and larder.

Climbing the front hall stairs brings us to the upper hall with two bedrooms on the right that are over the parlor. The first, overlooking the grounds behind the house, was my parents'; the second was the guest room. Turning to the left brings us into a hallway running along the back of the house. The first room on the right was shared by Atwood and Ned; Ella had the second to herself. Minnie and I shared the first room opening off the gallery over the ell, and on the end was the room occupied by our French governess, Mlle. Justine. Beyond her room the house ended, and just outside sat the huge, square, zinc-lined cistern that you will hear about later.

Surrounding the house on all sides were lawns and gardens and banks of exotic tropical plants near the fences, but our special source of pride were our Crèpe Myrtle trees.

Of course we had quite a few servants to take care of such an establishment, but only four of them were slaves and Papa gave the two oldest their freedom before the war. One was our cook Seline and the other our coachman Hippolite, known more simply as "Lite." The other two slaves worked in the gardens. Our housekeeper was a Creole of Color called 'Toinette, who was very efficient but not well liked by us children because of her appropriate but annoying obsession with cleanliness.

By the way, if the terms "Creole," "Free Woman of Color," and "Cajun" are confusing, I will explain them. "Creole" was the term used for a person of pure European blood, born in Louisiana. "Free Woman of Color," or "Creole of Color," referred to negroes who were not slaves, and "Cajun" meant a descendant of the Arcadians who were displaced from Canada and resettled in Louisiana in the middle of the 18th century.

And finally we had Mlle. Justine, our French governess whom we loved and who loved us, but who, being totally a city person and quite timid, could not bring herself to leave New Orleans with us in 1862.

My father was a businessman in an age and place where the opportunities to make large fortunes were there for the taking. Atwood, Jones & Company, the iron house that employed him in Pittsburgh, had sent him to New Orleans in 1838 to act as their agent. He was awestruck by the incredible volume of commerce being done in that combination sea and river port and soon went into business on his own. Until the completion of "Clinton's Ditch," otherwise known as the Erie Canal, the Mississippi River and its tributaries were the only practical paths of commerce to and from the entire midsection of America, and New

Orleans was at the gateway. The amount of factoring, brokerage, insurance and banking business that this traffic produced was phenomenal.

Here are some old letters that Pa wrote Grandma Violett back in Pittsburgh soon after he got to New Orleans.

ATWOOD, JONES & CO.
29 Natchez Street
New Orleans, Louisiana

April 21, 1838

Dearest Mother,

I arrived in New Orleans a week ago after a safe and most interesting passage down river to this extraordinary city. When I got to Memphis I transferred to a much larger steamboat, the "Belle of the West," and what a magnificent boat she is! She's twice as big and a third again as fast as the boat I left Cincinnati on, and far more luxurious.

There's a cabin for ladies with twelve small staterooms in the stern, a gentlemen's cabin amidships, and a bar and "social hall" forward. My cabin was tiny — barely room for a narrow berth, a corner shelf for basin and pitcher, and one small chair. You get some light through the ventilating transom over the door, but you are well advised to bring your own candle for reading.

Above it all is the pilothouse and the "texas" deck, all fenced and ornamented with clean white railings. On the texas deck you are twenty-five feet above the water and get the most magnificent view of the river and surrounding countryside. The further south we got, the more interesting the country became. Plantation after plantation lined the riverbanks with broad, flat fields of cotton heavy with bolls, or level green acres of sugarcane, and just back from the water's edge you see the tall pillared planters' homes. We stopped at many of them to deliver goods or take on passengers, so I was able to observe them closely, and I tell you I am very impressed with the prosperity that they demonstrate.

The quality of the owners and their families seems very

high, and I have been told that many of them are younger sons from established planters in the upper South, sent down with slaves and money to buy property. One gentleman, with whom I fell into conversation, confirmed that fact and boasted that with his original thirty slaves he made $12,500 cash money the first year merely by selling the wood cleared from the land to the steamboats for fuel at $2.50 a cord. He now owns sixty slaves and produces 500 bales of cotton a year and has a large plantation house with the finest furniture and decorations that Europe has to offer!

All the produce of these plantations and the goods that they purchase are funnelled through the port of New Orleans. In fact the whole country west of the Alleghenies does business with New Orleans one way or another. The amount of commerce is staggering!

I miss you and brother Edwin [my father's brother] and all the Englishes terribly, and I am so glad that I have the locket with the picture of you and father to comfort me. It was a fine gift and I will treasure it always. I know how you loved it, and I can feel that love glowing in it like a small ember. Bless you for your selfless generosity to your often unworthy son.

New Orleans is the most amazing city I have ever beheld; I don't know where to begin to describe it to you.

I first became aware of it on the morning of our arrival while we were still far up river, when the early rays of sunlight caught the golden dome of the St. Charles Hotel, the largest and finest in America they tell me, rising higher than the tallest church steeple in town. That golden gleam, like an enormous coin half buried in the green of the horizon, seemed a fine omen for the prosperity I hope to achieve here, and everything I have seen since confirms its promise.

The people are so colorful! Men wear skin-tight pantalons of light colored materials, drawn taut over the shoe top by a leather strap under the instep. The tails of their clawhammer coats reach down to their knees and are of bright colors, bottle green and royal blue being two favorites. Tall silk hats and gay flowered vests complete the dress of these human birds of paradise. The ladies' attire is colorful too, though in more muted tones, but unfortunately my knowledge of and vocabulary for the items of female attire is too limited to describe them. It is all a little startling to my more sombre Eastern tastes but so cheerful that I cannot criticize.

When it rains here the streets flood to a depth of several inches, and a wooden platform shoe called a "galoshe" is strapped on to keep the foot above the water. When it is dry the streets are so dusty that little negroes are hired to water them with scoops of water from the gutters, which, I am sorry to relate, also serve as the sewer system for the city. They run so full and freely that I have even seen little boys catching crawfish in these ditches within the city limits.

Colored women called "Marchandes" roam the streets with trays on their heads filled with dainties wrapped in paper in "picayune" piles, so called because each twist can be bought with the coin of that name. There is a great variety: celesto figs, tic-tac balls covered with open kettle sugar and pralines are the more predominant. On the corner of Canal and Chartres Streets there is a tiny soda establishment called the "Picayune," where for that price you can get a glass of soda and ginger syrup, or a thick honey and cream drink called "meade." Then there is the "cream cheese woman" who arrives at your house in the early morning hours selling little heart-shaped cheeses covered with fresh cream for your breakfast. They are delicious!

They are mad for the opera here and everyone goes, no matter what his social station. I have been once already and found it very different from what I have seen in New York. For instance, they have latticed boxes in the rear of the dress circle for people in mourning and "femmes enceintes." Afterwards, I was taken to a place called Vincent's where we had pâtés, brioche, éclairs, and meringues, washed down with a good chilled white wine.

I have not talked about business so far because I know that it has little interest for you, but I must say that never have I been anywhere, nor even heard of anyplace that had one tenth the potential for an active ambitious young man like myself. They say that there are 350 steamboats on the Mississippi now and I believe it, because there must be half that number here at all times. There are literally several miles of them tied up side by side, bow to the shore, and the acres and acres of levee area between them and the business district are piled as high as twenty feet with merchandise either coming or going.

Mr. Atwood has given me a rare opportunity in sending me here to put me in the way of making my fortune and I will never be able to express my gratitude adequately. Please give him my kindest regards and warmest affection at your next opportunity and say that I shall convey them myself by letter soon.

My love to you all and especially to you my dearest Mother from your adoring son —

William A. Violett

Three years later another letter made the following interesting announcement.

DYAS & VIOLETT — GROCERS
4 Tchoupitoulas Street
New Orleans, Louisiana

October 21, 1841

Dearest Mother,

. . . I completed my arrangements with Mr. Dyas last week and we are now partners in the firm of grocers whose letterhead I proudly display above. You may be sure that the money you lent me will be returned with interest soon, as business is very great, due, I believe, to our excellent location that is so convenient to our major customers which are the ships tied up to the levee.

My replacement as factor for Atwood & Jones has settled in well and I am relieved in that fact because I would not wish my leaving the firm to have caused them any inconvenience.

As you can see, Mally, Papa was quick to see the possibilities and put himself in a position to take advantage of them. I have never been too clear on the details of his affairs, although your uncle Atwood has tried to explain them often enough. Suffice it to say that after the grocery business they had to do with banking, real estate, and cotton. During the period from the time that he arrived in New Orleans in 1838 until the surrender of New Orleans to Captain Farragut in 1862 forced him to flee and abandon his business, he built up a very considerable fortune. Much of this he lost through confiscation by the Yankees for his activities in the Southern cause. But I am getting ahead of my story.

My personal memories of Papa before we went to Mobile are few. His presence in the house was small due to the demands of business on his time and the fact that like most well to do New Orleans families we spent from May to October in the North with our relations while he remained in the city.

Every summer my father would send Ma and us children north to avoid exposure to the almost annual epidemics of Yellow Fever in the city. This was no small concern. In the great epidemic during the summer of 1853, just a year before I was born, forty thousand people were afflicted and twelve thousand died. The city was like London in the plague years; cannons were fired continually to clear the air, barrels of tar burned at every street corner and bodies could be found on streets throughout the city. All through my childhood I heard horror stories about that summer.

Besides Yellow Fever, or "Bronze John," as it was called in New Orleans in those days, summertime brought an increase in the cholera that killed many infants including my little sister May, the child between myself and Ned, so there were compelling reasons to leave the city for the summer. People were called "Go-Aways" or "Can't-Get-Aways," depending on their financial abilities. Some could only afford to go to the other side of Lake Pontchartrain, but we were fortunate and traveled extensively throughout the North. My father would join us twice each summer for a brief time, but otherwise he felt that he had to stay in town for his business. He was a recovered victim of the Fever and had acquired immunity so we had no worry for him on that score, but my mother missed him horribly.

Those trips up the river were wonderful holidays for us children, though. We had relations in Kentucky, Cincinnati and in Alexandria, Virginia, and our three-month annual trips were divided between them. Ma loved to visit with her brothers and sisters, and we got on as well with our cousins as with each other. Our first moments together on each trip were always punctuated by the inevitable comments such as "My, how Atwood has grown," or "Ella certainly is becoming a real little lady!"

There were no railroads out of New Orleans until the end of 1860, so the only practical way to travel any distance was by steamboat. The Mississippi River steamboats weren't as palatial as they advertised, according to Ma, who found many deficiencies in them, but they were even more exciting than advertised to us children. "Floating birthday cakes" they were called, and I thought the term very appropriate. During the seven-day trip to Ma's home town of Louisville, Kentucky, there was the excitement of constantly changing scenes along the riverbank. Cotton fields, riverside hamlets barely distinguishable among the trees, little towns like Natchez and Vicksburg and cities like Memphis went by, and always there was the pulsing of the engines and the huge paddle wheels churning up the muddy brown water. Best of all sights along the shore we liked the large plantation houses, and we would all line the rail to study them as we passed by.

Some of the plantations like "Oak Alley" near Vacherie were favorites and we would anticipate their arrival. At Oak Alley the sand-bars forced the steamboat to run close in to the riverbank, so there was a brief moment as you passed when you could look down a long tunnel formed by the oaks over a lawn of shaded grass to the stately pillared and porticoed manor house at its end. Once I saw a woman and child, the plantation mistress and her daughter I supposed, standing by the railing on the gallery, two little white triangles against the blue-gray shade of the huge house behind them.

There was one deserted plantation house just up river from New Orleans that I especially liked. It was built in 1851 for Edmund Faronne by his father, who used the beautiful building to persuade his only son to give up his gay life in Paris and return to Louisiana. Edmund and his Creole bride had lived there for less than one year when they both died of Yellow Fever in the great epidemic of 1853. Edmund's father had the house boarded up, and the gardens around it reverted to the wild. It is still there today, sealed up for seventy years, so surrounded by jungle that only the dormers on the roof are visible from road or river. On a boat trip three years ago, I saw the dormer windows shining like gold in the afternoon sunlight. Romantic that I am, I wondered if behind those shutters the ghosts of Edmund and his wife continued in charade their roles in life.

Brother Atwood, who is seven years older than I, had much more practical thoughts about plantations. He knew much about their operation and what he didn't know he soon found out by diligent questioning. He was always like that about everything. I never knew anybody with so much curiosity. No matter what it was, he had to find out all about it. Older sister Ella, on the other hand, never asked about anything. She just pretended that she knew it all already. Ella was the perfect little lady, but I was a bit of a "Tom-Boy," and those steamboat trips up the Mississippi were made for me. I clambered all over the boat, driving our French governess Mlle. Justine wild with worry. Fortunately she was too busy with little Ned and Minnie to bother me much.

In Louisville we romped happily day after day with the many cousins our age until it was time to go on up the river to Cincinnati, where a fresh batch awaited us. These were some of the happiest times of my life; it seemed to me they would go on and on, and I would grow up, stop being a "Tom-Boy," and become the loveliest, most charming "Belle" New Orleans had ever seen. Later I would marry and have children just as my parents did, and maybe live as the mistress of one of those lovely old mansions seen from the river. I was serenely confident of my future.

You have only seen the old lady I have become. Let me try to describe what I was like as a child and young woman. I would send you some pictures, but since only a pitiful few of poor quality have survived, let me see what I can do with words.

I guess I'd better describe the whole family because to see me you will need them for background.

Mother (we all called her Ma, that was the way they did it in New Orleans — not Mummy the way they do today) was a short, slender woman with the biggest eyes you can imagine. They were so alive, so expressive of her feelings that it was impossible for her to be deceitful; her eyes always gave her away. When she looked at you you couldn't keep your eyes off her eyes, so it was pretty hard for us to fib to her, either. All through our lives there was a special feeling between Ma and myself. She used to call me "her little comforter." I didn't know what she meant at the time, but the long hugs and kisses that I got when she called me that made me feel so warm and secure. Later in our wandering, often homeless life those moments were "home" to me.

Well, Mally, the morning has fled and I can see Atwood and some of the others coming back over the field for lunch, so I will stop for now and begin another letter later. Much love from your devoted

Aunt Lily

Chapter 2

Camp Laurel
Tupper Lake
New York

July 11, 1925

Dear Mally,

Unfortunately the weather here has turned rainy and everyone is cooped up inside. I tried to write at the desk in the living room of the main house (the "Rec" room they call it), but the children were making too much noise so I retreated to one of the little sleeping cabins down by the lake and "set up shop" here. It is so peaceful with only the sound of the rain and the little wavelets lapping against the shore. André, the Camp's handyman, laid a fire in anticipation of fall guests, but I couldn't resist and lit it now. I love fires, especially with birch logs — they smell so fragrant and the cherry red coals on the snow white ashes are so pretty. I will apologize to André later. Now to work.

I was describing the family when I left off in my last letter.

Papa was a man of only average height, but he was a dominating presence in any company. He was not aggressive or loud-spoken — quite the contrary, he was usually a quiet, gentle man. It was the sense you had of his tremendous drive and energy that made him so noticeable in any group.

He couldn't abide long discussions about what to do in any uncertain situation. If there was a problem, he instantly found the crux of it and his solution was usually so logical that no further discussion was possible. His mind seemed to work so quickly that before you had finished a question he had anticipated the rest of it and was giving you your answer. Some people found this trait very annoying and said so. Then he would become very embarrassed because he meant no disrespect — his reaction was just instinctive.

He was thirteen years older than Ma and forty-two years of age when I was born. I remember him best as he was in the 1860's after we had been driven out of New Orleans and were living in Mobile. We saw much more of him then because he didn't have his work to go to. He was worn down from losing his business and from his all his efforts for the Confederacy and seemed much older than he actually was. He was almost bald and his well trimmed spade beard and curly mustache were streaked with white hairs and yellow tobacco stains from his incessant cigars which he smoked not only for the pleasure of the tobacco, but also to keep away the mosquitos that we endured eight months of the year. (There is a theory in New Orleans that I have never heard expressed elsewhere that the consumption of coffee produces an element in the perspiration that repels insects. Certainly those coffee-drinking, cigar-smoking gentlemen who spent the summer months in the city needed all the protection they could get!)

His wide mouth, half hidden by his mustache, had a pleasant set and his eyes were always kindly unless he was provoked — which seldom happened, but then watch out! When he was with us children he was tender and clumsily physically affectionate. He seemed unable to come right out and say he loved us, but he made us know it nonetheless. His concern for our well-being was almost obsessive. Should we come down with the slightest illness he would be nervous and complaining until we were well. He lectured us constantly on taking precautions during our summer travels. It was his way of letting us know that he cared. He would say, "Don't lean over the steamboat railing!" "Be sure to get off the street quickly if you hear fast hoofbeats!" "Don't play on top of the cistern, the top may be rotten and you could fall in and drown and no one would know!" That last admonition always frightened me because I was forever hiding up there. I would climb out the window of Mlle. Justine's room onto the cistern top and crawl to the edge where I could spy on everything in the yard below. The wooden top creaked warningly as I eased my body across it and I pictured the fatal plunge to a liquid death, but I was never deterred.

He and Ma were mad about entertaining. When we were in New Orleans, scarcely a week went by that there wasn't a party of some sort at the house. There were two kinds, one for just friends and the other for friends and musical people. Ma adored the opera and had made the acquaintance of a large number of performers, including the famous Adelina Patti, who made her début at the magnificent old French Opera House in the fall of 1860. She performed for almost fifty years before she retired. The last time I saw her was in 1893 on the same stage where she began. In 1860 Ma knew the manager of the Opera House, a M. Boudousquie I think, and persuaded him to bring his famous protégée to one of her musicales. Patti agreed on the condition that she would not be required to sing, because, as she frequently said, pointing to her throat, "What comes out here never goes in again." She came and she was charming; Ma was so pleased.

Brother Atwood adored Papa, and he was so obviously his father's favorite that we were often jealous. But then Atwood was so much older he seemed more adult than child to us. Later, when Papa died so suddenly and Atwood was twenty-one and had been in business with him for two years, he was awfully nice to us and Ma. He took over being the head of the household then and for a while Ma was only too glad to let him do it, she was so upset by Papa's unexpected death. Like Papa, Atwood would anticipate your question, but unlike Papa he was rather short of patience with us as children, and somehow that was how he always seemed to think of us no matter how old we became; we were his special charge. He loved people though and from all walks of life — French, American, negro or white, Yankee or Southerner, it made no difference to him.

Ella was my real problem as a child. She was always trying to boss me around; to get me to stop running about the house, to stop shouting to people in the street, to clean my hands and face and change my dirty dress, etc. . . . She was only four years older but you would have thought she was thirty, the way she pretended to know so much about how everything should be done, and she always told you just how to do it! Unlike Atwood with his many diverse friends, she had a small clique of carefully selected girl friends even hoity-toitier than she, and the black looks they gave me if I disturbed them would have shriveled a stove lid.

Fortunately she learned to restrain herself and we became quite close during the troubles that came later, although she never got over her tendency to try to improve people.

Little Ned was my favorite and Minnie a close second. They were respectively two and three years younger than me, but somehow we always found something to do together. Ned was small for his age and Minnie large, so strangers thought they were twins, especially during their younger years when Ned's dresses and hair could hardly be distinguished from Minnie's. Ned became the most beautiful boy I have ever seen in my life. Not only physically but spiritually. He radiated a kind of peace of soul and had a quiet perseverance that he developed overcoming his slowness with his studies that still touches me deeply when I think about it.

The other children at Miss Cena's (our neighborhood private school) used to taunt him so I wanted to destroy them all, and frequently tried. But Ned was neither cowed by their insults nor provoked to attack. He just smiled his knowing little smile and went on with what he was doing. You had to admire him, and in the long run — a very long run — he succeeded and could read and write as well as anyone. He was really very bright; it was just the reading and writing that he had trouble with. His death in 1919, when his dressing gown caught fire, was even more painful to me than any of the many family tragedies that preceded it, even Ma's death.

As Minnie grew up to be more than an adorable little baby, she began to show the intelligence that was to take her so far beyond the rest of us. She soon became the leader of her peers, organizing the other children into whatever game or enterprise she was constantly inventing. She wasn't bossy, she just always had some interesting way to fill in an otherwise boring time.

Even when she was quite young, Minnie had an unusual amount of concern for other people. She knew more about our neighbors than Ma did, and Ma did not lack feminine curiosity nor the means to gratify it. People were so touched when this little girl would say how sorry she was that Mrs. So and So's sister was sick, or how glad she was that Mr. X got that promotion at the Cotton Exchange. I don't think she was particularly inquisitive, she just seemed to understand better and listen more closely to what is always said in children's presence as though they did not understand the English language. And she was so exotically lovely with her huge dark eyes with their amber-brown irises and her full soft lips!

Her upper lip had the most pronounced "V" shape in the center, just under that little indent that Grandma Oldham used to call "God's fingerprint." Do you know that little fable? Grandma said that before babies are born they know all the secrets of life so they will not be afraid to come into the world, but then, just as they are born, God puts his finger on their lips to seal them, and that little indent under the nose is his mark. I think it is a lovely idea.

And then at last there was me, the middle child, always outdone by my older siblings and fighting to keep ahead of the two younger ones. Well, to keep ahead of Minnie anyway. I was aware quite early that Ned needed some pulling along. There's a picture of me and Ned when I was about five and he about three that I can see in my mind as though it were in front of me. I am sitting on a dining room style chair and Ned on a high chair. I say dining room "style" because the picture was not taken at home. That wasn't possible then. We were at the Stowe's Photographic Gallery in Louisville, Kentucky, while on our annual summer visit there. I was in a bad mood because my whole day had been ruined by this trip downtown (and I had had to get washed and dressed up, too!). I must admit now, though, it was worth it. Despite the grumpy look on my face, I think I was rather a pretty child in my frilly dress with a box bow in my hair and even my hated pantalettes didn't show too much. I can't say the same for Ned though. At three he was as fat as a butterball, and his shoulder-length hair looked just awful. By the time he was six, he had slimmed out and become very handsome; everyone remarked on the incredible change.

Well, I've reached that point where I think I'll end this writing session. The fire went out about ten minutes ago. I was too engrossed to save it, so the cabin has gotten quite chilly and my fingers ache from writing. I hope I haven't rambled too much. Next time I plan to tell you about the beginning of the War as we saw it in New Orleans and that terrible time when the city was surrendered to the North. You are such a dear to encourage me to go on with this and I am so flattered that you are

---

having your secretary copy my letters on her typewriter. It makes me feel like a real author! I will try to write more distinctly for her. Take good care of yourself and give my best love to Kathleen.

Fondly,
Aunt Lily

Camp Laurel
Tupper Lake
New York

July 14, 1925

Dear Mally,

This will probably be the last "letter" I will write on this project. I've been thinking it over and decided it gets too choppy this way. I can't remember what I talked about or didn't talk about in my previous letter, so I am going to try to write at least three times a week and then when I get enough together I'll send it to you all at once. If you will have your secretary send me a copy, I'll have a way then to check back. Also I've got a lot of letters and things in trunks in New York and New Orleans that I want to look at before I go too much further.

Back to 1860:

New Orleans before the war was one of the most beautiful and exciting cities in the world. The focal point was the levee that ran for almost five miles in a long crescent-shaped arc on the eastern bank of the river. Literally hundreds of steamboats and sailing ships were always tied up there and many others moored out in the stream. One of the loveliest sights could be found on the levee on a bright, sunlit morning after a stormy night when all the sailing ships would loose the sails on their yardarms to dry and all the steamboats would do likewise with their ensigns and signal flags. As far as the eye could see stretched an endless ribbon of white sails mixed with flags and pennants of every shape and color. It was achingly beautiful as they all fluttered in the morning breeze.

In the evening it was a favorite pastime for families to stroll down the levee and note the foreign flags from so many nations of the world on the ships tied up there. Sailors in every kind of uniform or dress came and went between mountains of cotton bales, sugar barrels and endless rows of boxed goods. New Orleans was the most prosperous city in America, and nowhere was it more evident than on the levee.

Just back from the levee was a wide work area and behind that the business houses — cotton brokerages, sugar factors, and banks. New Orleans was said to have more banks at that time than even New York. Inland from them were the residential areas of the city. Originally this land was part of the plantations existing there, but these were sold off and subdivided into building lots of generous dimensions. In the so-called Garden District where we lived, many purchasers like Papa's predecessor bought two or even three lots, then built on one and used the rest for garden areas with hedges of oleander and Spanish Dagger around the borders for privacy. Thus this part of the city before the war had an open, uncluttered feeling, and old plantation houses like "Three Oaks" and "Melpomene" on Carondelet Street still stood in regal splendor among their more modest urban neighbors.

The year before the war actually started saw New Orleans' gayest winter season in memory. Political storm clouds were rumbling on the horizon and occasional lightning flashes of physical violence were alarming, but generally speaking, Southerners were confident that a peaceful secession could be achieved, or that if war came they would prevail. Cotton was king! One Southerner could lick twenty Yankees! The North with its textile mills would never cut themselves off from the preeminent source of cotton in the world! Never!

Of course, as a six year old I was not really aware of all these details. Although it seems as though I actually remember all of what I am going to tell you next, in fact a lot of this was told to me afterwards. Still, having been there, one adopts other people's memories as one's own. Actually, I suppose, as far as my horizon would let me observe then, the world probably seemed much the same as always that winter.

As usual, mid June of 1860 saw Ma and her brood on their way north by steamboat up the Mississippi to Louisville and Cincinnati. Late in August, Papa joined us and we traveled by train to Alexandria, Virginia, where our uncle Robert Gray Violett lived. This was where Papa had been born in 1812, and he loved to come back to his boyhood haunts. When he was twenty and his father died, he moved with his mother and her sister, Mrs. William B. English, to Pittsburgh, Pennsylvania, where he found work in the then leading iron house west of the Alleghenies — Atwood, Jones & Company. (Your great uncle Atwood is a namesake for his employer.)

About a week after our arrival in Alexandria, we heard that the late King Edward (then Prince of Wales), who was a guest of President Buchanan at the White House, was to visit Mount Vernon. Uncle Robert was well connected in neighboring Washington and he arranged for us all to make an expedition to see the Prince embark. He was to be transported up river from the Navy Yard which was not far away on the other side of the Potomac. We crossed over and Uncle secured a position for us near the gangway to the ship. Buchanan being a bachelor, the honors of the White House were in charge of his niece, Miss Harriet Lane, and I remember that the ship taking the Prince up river was of the same name. How lovely, I thought, to have a beautiful ship named for you! The Prince, President Buchanan, Miss Lane, and all the other dignitaries paraded right past us and up the gangway. We all clapped politely and when the last of his entourage was aboard, the Prince stepped forward and gave us all a courtly bow and thanked us for our civility. How young and handsome he was with his fair sideburns and his opulent clothes.

In September we went up to New York, where we stayed at the St. Nicholas Hotel, the principal stopping place there for Southerners, and a prominent one, being located at the corner of Broadway and Spring Street, then the center of the hotel, theatre and shopping district. Most parades went up Broadway — I remember being awakened one night by an enormous commotion of shouting, the brassy light of torches reflecting off the ceiling of our bedroom. In my sleepy condition I thought the hotel was on fire, but it was only a political parade in support of the candidacy of Abraham Lincoln. It was very exciting. Ma let us watch from our window on the fourth floor as the "Wide Awakes" in their special capes and oil lamps paraded below. They would chant their slogan (which I forget), raise their lamps and shout a deafening

"Hoorah!" Papa said that there were actually fewer paraders than there seemed to be because they wanted to make an impression in that part of town, so they would duck into side streets and race back to join the tail of the parade and pass by again.

Atwood provided another indelible memory on that trip by getting into a fist fight with two other boys staying in the hotel. We were having tea in our parlor when in came Papa with Atwood, who was in a shocking state. His clothes were torn and his nose was bleeding, but he was grinning from ear to ear, as was Papa. Two boys, one from Charleston and the other the son of an intimate friend of Ma's from Cincinnati, had been ragging him on several occasions, and, as Atwood said, "I decided to have it out with them in the corridor and I was giving them 'Hail Columbia' when Papa came along and called out, 'Give it to them,' and I did." He was so proud of himself for having bested them. He still talks about it — I wager he would tonight if I set the scene for him.

That winter in New Orleans was, as I have said, particularly gay, but there was one party at our house that surely was the most delightful that I remember. Two first cousins of my mother's were visiting us from Louisville — Mary Prather and Susan Joyes and a friend of theirs, Emma Knight. Great Belles they were, all three, and what a good time they had!

One of the leading Beaux of that time was David Hennen. One night in late November, he and six other men engaged the entire orchestra of the Opera after the regular evening performance to serenade the three Belles from Louisville. When this great congregation arrived at our house, all there were asleep — that is until the music began. Then there was a frantic commotion as our parents and the three Belles quickly dressed. The entire house was illuminated and every window thrown open even though it was winter. With the band on the lawn outside, the Louisville belles, their beaux, and my parents danced until the musicians threw in the sponge. We children watched from the corner of the side gallery, wrapped in blankets against the chill, until, one by one, we fell asleep and Mlle. Justine carried us to our beds.

Even I was aware during that winter of 1860–61 that momentous things were happening in the world, though of course I didn't understand them. Many an evening I heard Papa and his friends in his study, loudly discussing the ever-mounting crisis. I couldn't hear the words, but the tone of their voices communicated great anxiety. My father was passionately against slavery, as were many Southerners, even a substantial number of plantation owners. They felt that the system had many disadvantages — the worst of which was that it was making the South into an agricultural monolith ruled by an almost feudal aristocracy that discouraged white immigrants and the development of the manufacturing facilities that were so prominent a feature of the North.

As a New Orleans businessman, Papa fervently believed that secession should be avoided at all costs, because, as it was later explained to me, New Orleans was more closely allied with the North through commercial river traffic than with the rest of the predominantly agricultural South. But the emotional issue of states rights was so powerful that reason was overcome by oratory. Papa said that the South did not fight to save slavery half as much as it fought out of dedication to a way of life. When the die was cast, all that men like my father could do was to throw in their lot with the majority and work as hard as they could to prevent their own predictions of disaster from coming true.

When Lincoln won the election in November everyone said, "Well, that's it," and I guess it was, because after much shilly-shallying South Carolina seceded just before Christmas. New Year's Day passed and another week went by during which no other states followed suit so Papa thought things might work out after all, but then in early January, 1861, Mississippi seceded, and by February 1st, Florida, Alabama, Georgia, Louisiana and Texas were out of the Union. Delegates met at Montgomery, drafted a constitution, and elected Jefferson Davis provisional President. The Peace Convention in Washington failed, the Union Navy blockaded all Southern ports and Southern forces under G.T.P. Beauregard fired on Fort Sumter in Charleston Harbor. The war had started.

More later; loads of love as always,

Aunt Lily

Camp Laurel
Tupper Lake
New York

July 27, 1925

Dear Mally,

Enclosed is my latest output. This is getting to be a rather large opus and I'm not halfway through. I feel sorry for your secretary.

As you can see from the letterhead we're still at the lake, but next week I'm leaving to visit with some friends in Lenox, Massachusetts, and I doubt that I'll have much time to write more until I go to stay with Atwood in New York City so don't expect anything for about a month. It's strange though, I've gotten to like writing and I'm going to miss it.

Give my love to Kathleen and you dear grandfather.

Fondly,
Aunt Lily

Chapter 3

I'm not going to retell the story of the war between the States one more heartbreaking time, only the little parts that we lived through. That is as much of that tragic period as I can stand, even at this great distance in time.

Your great grandfather Violett was a man of strong conviction. As I said before, he was against slavery and felt that secession would be a terrible mistake, so he did not ally himself with the Southern Cause until later that spring of 1861 when his home state of Virginia seceded and he felt honor bound to do so. (Southern honor — what a lot of folly was done for "Honor," but it was a compelling force in that society.) Once committed though, like many other wealthy Southerners, he equipped and armed a Company of troops who named themselves the "Violett Guards" and served throughout the war as part of the Army of Northern Virginia in the famous "Harry Hays Brigade." Few survived to see the surrender of Robert E. Lee.

After the company was formed and recruited, my father had a party at our house for the commissioned officers and for the non-commissioned officers, who were elected by the men. This peculiar Southern custom of having sergeants and corporals elected by the men they were supposed to lead was thought by many to have much to do with the lack of discipline for which Confederate troops were noted. It was a grand party, though. The soldiers looked so gallant in their uniforms and were so full of enthusiasm for the battles to come. Poor dears — they certainly got more than they bargained for.

That summer of 1861 we did not go north for obvious reasons. Instead we rented a cottage on the northeast side of Lake Pontchartrain.

This got us away from the worst of the Fever area but was still close enough to New Orleans so that Papa could feel we were within reach should anything unforeseen happen. We were there in July when the news of the Confederate victory at Bull Run was announced. Up and down the shore road you could see people talking in excited little groups and men clapping each other on the back as if the war were won and over. I remember I thought it was myself.

The summer drifted to an end without much significant military action that I can recall, and we returned gratefully to our home in New Orleans in October. It had not been much fun for us; we missed our cousins up north and didn't know many of the children living by the lake. It felt good to be back in the familiar school routine. The war grumbled on through the fall, Christmas and New Year's came and went and 1862 was upon us. What a year it was to be!

Suddenly, in late February, New Orleans was threatened from both the Gulf and the upper Mississippi. Federal ships had been blockading the river mouth for some time, but now the newspapers announced the arrival of Captain David Farragut, commanding the Union's Western Gulf Squadron, with orders to capture our city. We had strong batteries of guns on either side of the river at Fort St. Philip and Fort Jackson and a chain of huge cypress logs just downstream to make any ships coming up stop and try to clear a way through while being fired on by the forts. Also two big ironclads were being built in New Orleans, so we felt reasonably secure. So did our generals, I guess, because they sent all our troops north except those in the forts and a handful of troops under General Lovell.

On the night of April 24th, all these defenses came crashing down. Farragut's fleet fought its way past the forts through a carelessly unprotected hole in the log boom. Without the loss of a single major ship the fleet steamed up river and anchored the next morning opposite our defenseless city. Papa, who went down to see what was happening, said it was fearful to see all those huge warships so close to the levee with their terrible guns run out and pointing right at you in the most menacing way, knowing that at any minute they might fire.

Our ironclads had made no challenge to them for the simple reason that they had not been completed in time. Nor were there any Confederate troops of consequence around to resist a landing. General Lovell's men were second-raters and poorly armed at that. After setting fire to the cotton and other goods at the levee Lovell ordered his troops out of the city, and away they went, marching out through the groups of incredulous citizens flocking to the waterfront. Men as well as women in the crowd lining the levee that rainy morning wept with frustration at being let go so cheaply. It was so frustrating! In an instant, the richest city in the South was in Union control.

All the night before, we had heard the cannons from the forts down river and seen the gleam of rockets and Yankee mortars arcing high in the sky. We children were so terrified the Yankees were going to come and kill us all in our beds we crowded into our parents' room and spent a sleepless night there. About eleven o'clock the light of fire close at hand, seemingly from the levees, sent us into a panic of fear that the Yankees had in fact already arrived, but a young man running past in the street told Papa that it was our own soldiers burning supplies to keep them from the enemy. From this we knew that the forts had failed, and we prepared for the worst.

Next morning, Ma kept us all in the house while Papa went down to the levee to get the latest news. The front gate was shut and barred behind him, and all the shutters were drawn. About eight-thirty in the morning the church bell in Christ Church sounded the alarm that Farragut's fleet had arrived. Outside in the streets, we could hear distant commotions and people shouting, "The Yankees are here!"

Papa returned and told us what he had seen and heard. He was badly shaken. He said that Farragut's ships showed some shell holes and torn rigging so our boys had done some fighting, but none seemed to be badly damaged. There were drunken slaves and white trash looting all through the business district. Yankee officers had come ashore and asked the mayor to surrender. The mayor had tried to put it on to General Lovell, but Lovell refused the responsibility and left; so the Federal Commander notified the mayor to evacuate all women and children from the city within twenty-four hours. He refused on the obvious grounds of its impossibility, so finally the Federal officer took his squad of marines with fixed bayonets to Lafayette Square and personally hauled down our flag and hoisted the Yankee flag in its place. The mayor told the crowd to go home and stay off the streets.

Then Papa took Ma into another room where they remained for a long time. When they returned Papa told us that we were going to leave our home and go to live in Mobile, Alabama, for the time being. I'll never forget that phrase "for the time being." We thought he meant for just a few weeks. In any event, go we must! Papa had been too active in the Confederate cause to risk internment under the new laws passed by the United States Congress, and he felt the situation in the city would be too dangerous for the family to remain there. In that assessment he was to be proved only too correct.

The rest of the day and most of the night were spent in packing what few things we would be able to take in our two carriages and in hiding as best we could the valuables we would have to leave behind. Ma was beside herself at the thought of leaving her home and possessions to the Yankees, but she kept her composure most of the time. Only occasionally would she stop what she was doing, drop into a chair and hide her crying in her hands. Papa made a hurried trip to his office in the afternoon and returned with a belt of gold coins he had providentially set aside for such an emergency.

The turkey rugs were rolled up and put in the loft over the help's quarters; the family portraits of the Oldhams and the Martins were taken off the walls and put in a space between the ceiling of Papa's dressing room and the roof; the library was stripped of Papa's collection of beautiful vellum-bound books, which were carted off to some other hiding place. There was nothing to be done with the furniture, but Papa thought of a hiding place for the silverware that proved a very successful one. Silver pieces were wrapped tightly in pillowcases and sheets, and after dark we passed the bundles out the window of Mlle. Justine's room at the back of the house to Papa and Atwood, who stood waiting on top of our cistern. They lowered the bundles gently and quietly into the water, being careful to see that they lay to the rear of the tank where they would be less likely to be noticed by anyone making a casual inspection. When all was done Papa artfully draped a fallen limb from one of the crèpe myrtle trees over the hatch cover to give the impression that it had been long shut.

Supper in the bare-walled dining room that night was a quiet, dark affair — dark because Papa would only let us have enough candles to see our food. He wanted no bright display to attract attention from the hostile streets. We went to our rooms as though in a strange house, all dark and bare and shuttered-in — a stranger's house in a stranger's city. New Orleans was no longer ours.

Fortunately the infamous General Ben Butler did not land many of his ten thousand troops until a few days later, so we had time to leave New Orleans unhindered. That was one of the saddest moments in my life. Although we eventually returned to our home in New Orleans, our life as a family there was never the same again. No, when we packed what we could in the two carriages and locked the doors and shutters, that was the end of an era. I remember that we all sat in the carriages for a long time while Papa made a tour of the grounds. When he came back he slowly and reluctantly swung the heavy cast iron gates shut behind him. He climbed into the lead carriage and we drove off down the dusty street in silence. No one could trust his voice to speak.

I remember that morning in late April sixty-three long years ago as if it were yesterday. It was very hot for that time of year and dry — so dry everything looked dusty, even the leaves on the trees. As we passed through the streets all the houses presented us with silent, shuttered walls. No people could be seen except others like ourselves, part of an endless stream of people leaving the city — some in carriages or wagons, some on foot pushing handcarts filled with their possessions. There were few of the latter sort though; most of the poorer people were willing to take their chances in an occupied city. When we got to the edge of town, you could see a long line of vehicles in dusty procession towards the east. Ahead was nothing but unsettled empty countryside; behind, New Orleans lay shining in hazy sunlight, a little smoke from the fires on the levee still rising as evidence of the city's distress. Finally, after about an hour, the road took a turn that blocked the town from view, and we were alone and on our own.

It was a long, difficult journey to Mobile since there were so many other travelers going our way and the accommodations for food and lodgings so overtaxed by this sudden rush of people. When we were well clear of the town, Papa got out of our carriage and, taking Atwood with him, walked ahead of the horses with his arm around Atwood's shoulder. I could see they were planning something by the way they gestured. They came back to us, and Papa said that he would ride ahead on the extra horse and find lodgings for the night so that when we caught up the arrangements would be made before the whole horde of refugees arrived.

We followed this plan every day, and it worked well. We spent our nights either at small country inns or crowded into rooms in a farmhouse. We marveled that so few of our fellow travelers thought of such a simple expedient.

When we arrived in Mobile ten days later, there was a similar overdemand for accommodations, but Ma had a distant cousin we prevailed upon to put us up until we could find a permanent residence. We found a small cottage and stable on the edge of town for rent at an exorbitant sum. The local landlords were taking advantage of the situation, but fortunately several months before we left New Orleans, Papa had been part of a syndicate that was successful in smuggling a shipload of cotton past the blockading Yankee squadron. By the same ship he had sent directions to Baring's, his cotton agent in London, to hold his share of the profits and send him a letter of credit to a bank of his designation. It was a sizeable amount of money, enough to keep us all through our exile.

We soon settled into a routine of life in our new abode which was comfortable enough though far from our usual style. Strangely, the same Miss Cena who had run our school in New Orleans was in Mobile with her family. Finding a good number of her former pupils in the vicinity, she set up a school and we all took up where we had left off a month previously. It was very reassuring to have this part of our New Orleans routine restored to us, and we applied ourselves to our lessons with a most unusual energy.

Atwood, then fifteen, was frantic to get into the war, while Ma was equally frantic to keep him out. She was loyal enough to the cause, but you must remember that she had lost three children already to childbirth and disease. Papa as usual came up with a solution acceptable to both parties, and within a month Atwood was enrolled at the Alabama Military University at Tuscaloosa, where he spent the next two and a half years. As it turned out he was far from being as safe as Papa had promised Ma, but I'll get to that later.

Soon after we settled in at Mobile, we began to get disturbing news from New Orleans. Things happened there that have been glossed over by the historians, but I think they were important out of all proportion to their local nature. What happened in captured New Orleans was as important to the rest of the Confederacy as news of a kidnap victim is to his family. Not only did Southerners with family and friends in the city agonize over their cruel treatment, but they saw in New Orleans their own future should the Confederacy fail. It was not a pretty picture.

Because of its early capture, New Orleans was the first place in the South where the slaves were freed. Many slaves chose, wisely, I think, to remain with their owners; others, after running off in the first frenzy of liberation, begged to be taken back (though because of their new liberated status, it was difficult for slaves either to remain with or to return to their masters), making the Union officials feel thwarted in their mandate to free the slaves. They insisted on contracts of employment that were impossible for the former owners to honor, and the whole relationship of the classes was thrown into confusion.

The most galling change was the presence of a large number of negro soldiers in the Yankee army of occupation, not only men recruited in the North, but local ex-slaves enlisted right in New Orleans. The sight of them ordering white people around was more than white Southerners, rich or poor, could bear! Never had they imagined such insult, degradation and humiliation as they felt then, especially the women. I think the women of New Orleans, in the simplistic reasoning of women anywhere, felt betrayed by the Confederacy for letting their city be so easily taken. Then this further degradation was imposed on them, and there built up in them a flood of anger and frustration that had to spill out somewhere.

I remember reading in one of Grace King's books about that period in New Orleans. She said that it seemed a trifling consideration how women felt in a war, but since children feel much as their mothers do, the mothers, in a sense, dictate history in advance. To the men belongs the war; to the women belongs the peace that follows it. What "Beast" Butler did to the women of New Orleans during his six-month reign, and the reaction of those women, which froze into an implacable hatred of all things Northern for the rest of their lives, is ample proof of her analysis.

The incident that epitomized the nature of the Butler régime was the hanging of a sixteen year old boy called Mumford. A barge crew from the Federal flagship had raised the United States flag over the U.S. Mint building and some wild-spirited lads had immediately climbed the flag pole and torn it down. Taking it to the city hall where the mayor was in negotiation with the Federal officers, the boys mutilated the flag and one of them, namely Mumford, threw it through the mayor's window to land at the officers' feet. When this was reported to Butler, he said, "I will make an example of that fellow by hanging him." Farragut, who was present, replied, "You will have to catch him and then hang him." "I know that," said Butler, "but I *will* catch him and hang him." And he did.

Mumford was arrested, quickly tried and condemned to hang. The city was horrified, and every attempt was made to obtain mercy, but to no avail. The boy was hanged on a gallows dramatically placed in front of the Mint where his offense had taken place.

Predictably, this had the reverse of the effect intended. Instead of the hanging coercing respect for the Union flag, it made the women of New Orleans, without I think any collusion, go out of their way (literally) to show their revulsion for what the flag had been made to symbolize. They walked out into the street to avoid passing under a flag hanging over the "banquette" (or sidewalk as it is called elsewhere). As there were Union flags displayed all over the city to remind the citizens of their conquered status, there were many opportunities for the ladies to make their point. Equally adamant that the Union flag should be respected, Butler retaliated by having flags hung in strings across whole streets and posting details of soldiers to seize women who sought to avoid the ordeal and compel them to pass under the hated emblem. Even then the women would cover their heads with a shawl or a parasol in token defiance. This all seems faintly ridiculous now, but feelings then were running very high and this was one of the few ways they could be expressed.

I just went over and found a copy of Grace King's book in Atwood's library, and I want to quote a passage about the Mumford incident that I remembered because it touched me so when I first read it.

> . . . for twenty years after that day [of the hanging] there wandered through the streets of New Orleans a thin, wrinkled, bent, crazy woman, wandering always, it seemed, as if by command, across groups of children on their way to and from school. The children never ran and shrank from her as from most lunatics. "Hush!" they would say; "She is Mumford's mother." "But she is not Mumford's mother," many would insist. "She only thinks she is Mumford's mother."

"She is Mumford's mother all the same," would be the reply.

During the school hours, the poor woman would wander in the business thoroughfares, and when tired she would crouch in the corner of some house-step and sleep, and passers-by would slip a coin into her lap (she never begged awake). "That is Mumford's poor mother," they would explain.

You must remember, Mally, that mentally New Orleans was totally unprepared for such unchivalrous treatment as it received from Butler. There was no historical precedent like the Great War to give them warning. The Mumford boy's hanging was just the beginning; far worse was to come.

Every family had to bring in a list of all their possessions and sign an oath as to their allegiance — to either the Union or the Confederacy. There were no allowances for mixed feelings. To neglect to include all possessions on your list was "high treason," for which the offender would be imprisoned. Even securities and valuables in bank boxes had to be included, and all these properties were subject to confiscation. Armed sentinels placed at the doors of suspected rebel sympathizers recorded the names of all visitors. House searches were made, and it was a terrible shock for children to see their mothers' armoires invaded and the contents dumped on the floor to be pawed through by negro Federal soldiers.

Those who took the "iron clad oath" of allegiance to the United States did not have to fear confiscations, but they were ostracized by their friends and no decent tradespeople would serve them. Those who declared for the Confederacy or even declared kinship to soldiers of the Confederacy were put out of the city with nothing but the clothes on their backs. This actually happened to many hundreds of women and their children who refused to perjure themselves; they were forced to depend on the charity of family or friends for their survival. Many, less brave or less fortunate in their connections in the Confederacy, perjured themselves and had to bear that humiliation as well as all the rest.

Every type of person was arrested, even clergymen for not praying for the President of the United States, and newspaper editors for publishing stories or articles deemed "favorable to Confederate interests."

A woman was arrested and jailed for laughing while a Federal funeral procession went by.

The battle of the flags went on, and Southern women were brought to the Provost Marshall for wearing miniature Confederate flags in their hair or fichus — one, even, for having a bonnet with flowers of the Confederate colors done to suggest the flag. To sing "Dixie" or "The Bonnie Blue Flag" was to invite arrest. "The venom of the she-adder is as dangerous as that of the he-adder" was a legend that General Butler had printed and hung in his office. The list of "crimes" goes on and on, but they become repetitious.

There was, as Grace King put it, "a carnival of confiscations and forced auctions." Butler and his subordinates seized the handsomest residences in the city for their own use and, if occupied, threw the owners out into the street. If you were a "registered enemy" and forced to leave, you could sell your personal possessions, but you would be lucky to realize one one hundredth of their value. Our house was taken for a residence by Federal officers and almost everything but the silverware that Papa and Atwood hid in the cistern was gone when we returned after the war. No, that's wrong, the paintings were there over the false ceiling in Papa's study, but they were much mildewed and foxed. Only the Oldham miniatures survived undamaged.

The climax of Butler's régime came with his infamous Order No. 28, which stated that any woman who by word, gesture, or movement, insulted or showed contempt for the United States or its officers would be regarded and held liable to be treated as a woman of the town plying her vocation. The world reaction to this indignity was so strong that it caused Butler's recall and his replacement by General Banks, who, while a harsh reconstructionist, was above the contemptible, almost insane actions of "Beast" Butler. Banks began the program of civil reconstruction of the South that was to choke us with Union officials for the next decade, but all that came later.

Chapter 4

In Mobile, we seemed to exist in a state of isolation from all the things in the world that were important to us. We were completely cut off from Ma's relatives in Louisville and Cincinnati and we had little accurate information on the military situation, although we were certain that it was not going well. News of possible foreign intervention, the only thing that Papa felt could save the Confederacy, could be inferred only from the meagrest scraps of information. The tension, the frustration, the constantly depressing bad news took its toll of all of us, but especially Papa.

Papa was too old for active military service and in any event had no qualification or inclination for it, but he was idle in Mobile and yearned to be of use to the South. Not so much to serve the Confederacy, but to ease the suffering of the sick and wounded men in the Confederate armies. The hospitals available to these men were woefully inadequate in number, and many so-called hospitals were such in name only. They were buildings crammed with wounded men and lacked almost everything but shelter to ease the suffering. What few doctors and "nurses" were present worked until they collapsed. There were no medicines or opiates for pain; bandages and dressings were improvised; there was not even sufficient food or water. These "hospitals" were the greatest blot on the "Honor" of the Confederacy. That the South should call on its young men and boys to fight and be so unprepared to deal with their wounds was beyond bearing. Papa decided that this was where he would spend his energies.

I remember a story he told us by way of illustration. The son of a business friend of his was seriously wounded fighting in Virginia. The

Confederate lines were overrun, and he found himself a prisoner. He was taken to the rear and treated in a Yankee hospital, and because of that prompt, efficient treatment, he survived despite the gravity of his wound. Papa's friend had a second son who was less fortunate. Shot through the fleshy part of the calf while fighting in Tennessee, he lay three days unattended outside a Confederate hospital, during which time his leg went gangrenous. He died during the attempted, unanaesthetized amputation. He was sixteen years old!

Papa was in tears when he finished that story, and his voice broke when he came to the part about the boy being only sixteen. It was the only time I ever actually saw him cry.

He thought for days what he might do and came up with a plan that he felt might work. He talked it over with some of his prominent friends in Mobile and they agreed to help.

The basic idea was simple: to trade Southern cotton which the North so desperately needed in exchange for hospital supplies, medicines, blankets, shoes and other items unavailable in the South that would ease the suffering of its soldiers without materially helping its military efforts. Papa and his backers made many trips to Richmond and even crossed the lines under a flag of truce to negotiate with the highest officials in Washington. After many months of work they were successful, and full agreement was reached between Richmond and Washington. The exchange was to be made in Mobile Bay. The supply ships from the North arrived and were awaiting the signal to make the transfer when official word arrived from Richmond revoking approval of the exchange. Blockade runners, those black-hearted vultures feeding on other people's suffering, saw in the exchange a threat to their profits and, through their influence in high places, forced its cancellation.

Robert E. Lee went into the history books as a gallant Southern general who fought brilliantly with an outnumbered and outprovisioned army. He suffered no disgrace when he surrendered at Appomattox.

Jefferson Davis and his cabinet did the best they could with what they had, most people say.

Who, then, were the men responsible for the awful negligence that resulted in those Confederate "hospitals"? Who were the men who destroyed my father's plan to help those suffering soldiers who gave everything and got such an awful reward? Where was Southern "honor" that it could let this happen? For all its boasting, Southern Honor can claim no higher place than the quality of the hospitals it provided for its heroes.

Papa never spoke these thoughts in front of me, but I am sure they were in his mind. How bitter he must have felt! How I wish that I had known then and could have done something to make him feel better, but I was just a child of ten and not wise enough to understand all this or recognize his pain for what it was.

It was at this time that Papa sat down at the little table in the corner of the kitchen and wrote, on a small piece of lined paper, his last will and testament. Fortunately, he lived to make another, more formal one, but that piece of paper has been preserved by Atwood all these years as a reminder of the depths of Papa's depression at that dreadful time. It reads in part as follows:

Mobile, Alabama
February 28th, 1864

I, W.A. Violett, make this my last will whereby I shall, with the help of God, do justice to my wife and children . . .

. . . I owe no man anything, and whatever is saved out of the wreck of my fortune is solely for their benefit as my sole heirs under the laws of Louisiana . . .

. . . Provided only, that my dear Mother, Catherine G. Violett, shall be paid an annual allowance of five hundred dollars for the rest of her life . . .

. . . The Value of my Estate on the 1st May 1862 was about half a million of dollars consisting of Real Estate . . .

. . . The assets of my commercial firm are all in the hands of my partner W.C. Black, except the following:

Gold, brought out of New Orleans by the Bank of Louisiana during the occupation of New Orleans by Federal troops . . . certificates of deposit for which are in the names of Mrs. Sarah K. Rickarby and Mrs. Jane Black . . . Neither of these ladies has any beneficial interest in said certificates . . .

Papa went on to list, as best he could, the various assets and properties that he had acquired since he came to New Orleans in 1838.

It was as though by setting down their descriptions on paper, he was making them a safe reality, whereas in truth he had no idea whether they were still his or not.

He had failed to bring off the trade of cotton for medical supplies, he had spent more of his own money than he could afford in the attempt, and he was worried sick about what would become of us all in those chaotic times.

That was in 1864 when the fortunes of the Confederacy were sinking fast. Three years of struggle and inept management had exhausted its resources. There wasn't an able-bodied man that wasn't already in service, the paper currency was almost worthless, and yet Jefferson Davis clung to his dream of empire. Anyone could see that we were under siege. We could make small morale building offensive sallies, but they had no hope of significant victories. They could only hide for a moment the inescapable fact that the North was just too strong in every way.

All that was left to us territorially was described in the newspapers with great optimism and fanciful imagery as the "Head and Heart of the Confederacy. Richmond is the Head and Atlanta is the Heart; Lee is the Helmet and Johnston is the Shield." Pretty poetry, but the weary Army of Northern Virginia and the depleted Army of Tennessee were our only two major fighting forces. Connecting them was a pitifully thin railroad line with only a few Confederate forces to defend it.

In the fall of 1864, Sherman's march to the sea saw the fall of Atlanta and Savannah. In November Abraham Lincoln was re-elected, ending the hope that a peace party might take over and offer a compromise that could be acceptable to Southern "Honor." Petersburg, the key to the defense of Richmond, was under heavy siege. Except for isolated, well defended pockets like Mobile, the boundaries of the Confederacy had been reduced to the southern third of Virginia and the northern third of North Carolina, with about 100,000 soldiers against half a million Yankees. All the rest of the original Confederate States of America were under Federal control.

Mobile itself was now threatened. It had been left alone by the Union until that time because it was considered the best fortified city in the Confederacy, with fifteen thousand men to defend itself. Because these men were thus denied to our armies, the Yankees deemed it better to leave them so employed. We were under loose blockade by a Yankee squadron in the Gulf, but our ships controlled the Bay itself. When the Federal supply ships left with the precious medical supplies still in their holds, they were soon replaced by others carrying a more lethal cargo. On the 5th of August, 1864, Admiral Farragut and a strong fleet steamed into Mobile Bay and immediately attacked Fort Gaines. Farragut took it, forced the surrender of Fort Powell, and defeated our small fleet of ships — all in a period of only three days! Once again we could look out from the rooftops and see those very same warships that had lain so ominously in the Mississippi opposite New Orleans. Were we to have to leave Mobile too?

Fortunately not, for Ma and Ned were both ill. No further attack was made on us until the spring of 1865. The fighting then lasted from the seventh of March until the twelfth of April. It was all to the east of the city so we were never under personal attack, but we saw and heard grim evidence of it in the form of wounded men brought in for what treatment we could give them, and always there was the sound of cannon and rifle fire to the east. On the twelfth our dapper little mayor surrendered the city to General Granger. Papa figured that there was no point in our leaving Mobile, even if there were any place to go. All of his business and properties had already been confiscated and though he might face imprisonment if he stayed in Mobile, he said that he thought it would all be over before they got around to his case.

Now we began to get a taste of the occupation problems we had avoided in New Orleans. Fortunately, they were of a far milder sort, and anyway we were so mentally beaten down by that time that we endured it all with numb resignation. Our greatest concern was that we had had no word from Atwood in over a month, and because we had heard that General Wilson's cavalry had overrun all of northern Alabama, Ma was beside herself with worry. There was little Papa could do to calm her fears because General Granger had imposed strict controls forbidding travel, and of course there was no regular mail service at all. The city had to be supplied, though, and Papa would go down to the markets every morning to try to glean some news relative to Atwood from the men that drove the wagons. Some letters were being smuggled into the city by these teamsters, and Papa hoped that Atwood, if he had survived, would either come to Mobile in person or send a letter. But no word came, and day by day we began to lose hope that we would ever see him again.

Petersburg and Richmond fell, Jefferson Davis and his cabinet leaving behind them a burning city and an angry mob that had to be clubbed out of the way by Confederate troops to get the Presidential party on a train out of the city. Not more than a week later, Robert E. Lee and Joseph E. Johnston* surrendered their armies in Virginia and in North Carolina and it was finally all over.

In early May, Jefferson Davis, abandoned along his route of flight by all the members of his cabinet except his Postmaster General and by then "persona non grata" to his fellow Southerners, was captured in a little town in south Georgia. It was not a dignified surrender as would have done some honor to the occasion of the eclipse of the last light of the Confederate States of America. That would have been some solace to the countless Southerners who survived to read of it, but even that was to be denied us.

Our President was taken dressed in women's clothing in a pathetic attempt to disguise himself and avoid capture! How could he have done this cowardly, disgraceful thing? I never believed that story that it was just his wife's coat and he picked it up and put it on by mistake! How could there be such a thing as Southern Honor when a man in so high a position of trust would act so disgracefully? We wept with rage and shame. I have never understood how he regained his position as a leader in Southern society, but he did. Atwood knew his family quite well and, like many many other Southerners, would hear no evil spoken of him. When he died Atwood was chairman of one of the committees in charge of his obsequies.

Coincidence is a curious thing. The Union flag raised over the capitol building in Richmond after its capture was the very same one raised over General Butler's headquarters in New Orleans three years earlier, and the last Confederate unit to surrender was a New Orleans Company located at Shreveport, Louisiana, at the time. It had been organized and outfitted in New Orleans in 1861. It all seemed so "circular" to me.

By mid May restrictions had been relaxed on travel and Papa deemed it was time for us to return to New Orleans. Ma was worried

---

* *Author's note:* Although Lee did surrender April 9, Johnston did not formally surrender until April 26.

about Yellow Fever, but Papa said we would just have to chance it. If he was to salvage anything from the ruins of his business he had to go there at once, and he did not dare leave us on our own. Besides, our supply of cash was running down to nothing, accelerated by the terrible inflation. There used to be a saying that when you went shopping you needed a satchel of Confederate money to buy what you could carry in your wallet.

Ma was worried that Atwood would come to Mobile and find us gone. What if he was sick or wounded — what would he do? She saw him weak and helpless, perishing at the hands of the bands of scallywags that roamed the South. It was no use though; Papa was adamant that we must go, so we left messages with trusted residents of the city who promised to be on the lookout for him and started back to New Orleans.

We had three choices as to how to travel. We could try to find a ship to take us along the coast; or we could go by train up to Meridian, Mississippi, then across through Jackson to Vicksburg, where we might get on a steamboat going down the river; or we could start out going by horse and carriage with all our possessions in a wagon behind and see what happened.

Coastal shipping had been so disrupted by the blockade that it was impossible to secure passage in the near future, and train service was also chaotic. There was no way of finding out what the situation was on the Mississippi, so Papa decided that we would go by road until a better form of transportation presented itself. There were no decent roads along the coast, so we would take the road that roughly followed the railroad tracks until we got to Jackson, Mississippi, and then decide whether to go on to Vicksburg for a steamboat or continue by road down through Mississippi. As it turned out we made the whole trip by road.

The whole South seemed to be reshuffling its population, and what a scruffy, threadbare lot we all were. It was like the beggars' parade in that French play, only this was no comedy. They used to say that Southerners could endure pain better than most, but either that was a vain boast or the poor men that we saw jolting along in springless wagons like so many living logs suffered pain of new depths and dimensions, because they were unable to hide their agony. Were some of these the clean, confident, even strutting, young men in dashing uniforms who attended that party my parents gave in 1861 for the "Violett Guards"?

The unwounded looked old beyond age, their complexions a

matching shade of their tattered gray uniforms; even their mood seemed the same sombre, joyless color. They were not glad to be going home. They came neither from victory nor honorable terms of peace, but from complete unconditional capitulation. Ahead of them lay only momentary physical rest and then an uncertain future in which only one thing was certain — grinding effort to somehow earn a livelihood under the ever-present supervision of an army of occupation, an army of victorious white Yankees and liberated negroes eager to exercise power over their former masters, a power made absolute by their Union uniforms and the 13th Amendment.

Day after day we bumped and rattled slowly, oh so slowly, in a mixed stream of soldiers and returning refugees like ourselves — a shabby, dust-covered, dispirited family of six longing only for the journey to be over and for some good news of Atwood. On this return journey Papa could not ride ahead because we no longer had Atwood or an extra horse, and there were too many evil-looking rascals on the roads for an unescorted woman and four young children. Don't forget that despite the length of my narrative we hadn't aged greatly since we left New Orleans. In 1865 Ella was fifteen, I was eleven, Ned was nine, and Minnie eight — hardly an intimidating group, but Papa had his Colt revolver so we felt reasonably safe.

I really don't remember how long the trip took. It seemed as though we were on the road forever, but finally one morning there we were on the northern shore of Lake Pontchartrain near the town of Mandeville, only a twenty-mile ferry ride from home. We waited two days for our turn on the ferry, two days where our longing to be home was increased one hundred fold by our proximity. So near and yet so far, as they say. Finally it was our turn, and we lined up with the others due for that crossing, in a perfect frenzy of apprehension lest some last minute difficulty should arise with the loading and we would be told that we must go back and wait again. Then we were safely on board, silently defying any power on earth to dislodge us.

Four hours later, as the sun was setting, we were ashore once more and only six miles from the city. To speed our progress Papa and Ella walked beside the carriage to lighten the load on the horses, but such was our condition that it was an hour and a half before we arrived at the corner of Fourth and Prytania Streets. In the twilight the house seemed intact and miraculously empty. At least we were not forced to deal with Yankee officers quartered there, as we had anticipated. Ma remarked how fortunate that was, but Papa replied grimly that he feared there had to be a reason for that and he proved to be correct, as we later found out.

Then the most unexpected, wonderful, joyous thing happened. Papa had just opened the cast iron front gate when we all saw through the dusty fanlight over the front door the glimmer of a candle being carried down the front hall staircase. Apprehensive as to who it might be, we stopped and waited in a group by the gate. The door swung open, and there, standing with his hand cupped around the flame and the light of it full on his face, was dear brother Atwood! It was such a surprise and shock that it took a moment of stunned inaction for our minds to comprehend what our eyes had seen. It was Minnie who reacted first and, flinging the bundles in her hands in the air, rushed to Atwood and nearly knocked him off his feet. Then we were all around him talking all at once, hugging him, kissing him, feeling him for possible hidden injuries in one great explosion of joy and relief. When the storm subsided, we were too weak to do more than collapse in one clump on the front steps. Ma was crying in almost hysterical relief, and the faces of the rest of us were not much less wet.

The first thing we had to know was what had happened to Atwood since his last letter some four months earlier, and he told us despite repeated interruptions and questions. He was literally the center of attention. We were so tightly pressed together around him, it was as if we thought he might somehow escape us, but he couldn't have moved if he'd tried.

What his story boiled down to was this. Wilson's Cavalry, the leading edge of a strong Federal swing from Tennessee down through Alabama and into Georgia, had been ordered to make a raid on Tuscaloosa and burn the public stores, foundries, bridges, and the Military Institute that Atwood was attending. If possible they were to capture the students and faculty. The Institute was aware of their proximity and on April 3, 1865, its scouts reported back that a detachment of cavalry was headed toward the town. Although they could muster only three companies of boys (none older than nineteen), the cadets drove the enemy through the town and across the river before the Yankees were reinforced. There was hot fighting then and a number of the boys were wounded. Whether any died Atwood did not know because they were forced to retreat and leave their wounded comrades on the field.

The cadets immediately set out to march to the nearest safe rail-head some fifty miles to the southeast at Marion, Alabama. Speed was essential to avoid capture, and they covered the difficult terrain in five days. Each carried gun, ammunition, knapsack and blanket roll. They were given only two rations daily of bacon and cornbread washed down with stream water. A few boys whose strength gave out had to ride in the wagon, but Atwood said how proud he was to be among those still on their feet when they reached Marion. So was Papa, and he reached over, put his arm around Atwood, and hugging him, said he guessed it wouldn't hurt if his Papa gave him a kiss on the cheek to welcome him home.

Later we learned that there had been near encounters with Union troops out of Trion and Centerville, captured several days before Tusca-loosa, but the cadets had remained undetected and passed on. The Cadet Corps was disbanded at Marion, where the people of the town divided the three companies between them for meals, as the government had no stores there. They remained in Marion for a week and then were fur-loughed for thirty days to go home, rest up and get reclothed, as they were in pretty bad shape in that respect.

Atwood felt it would be more prudent to stay with his comrades than venture alone through uncertain territory to Mobile, so he obtained permission to go by train to Meridian, Mississippi, where he had heard an Artillery Company from New Orleans was presently stationed. When he arrived, he met an officer who was a friend of Papa's and borrowed $100 from him. With this windfall his first investment was a breakfast of ham and eggs, biscuits, and real coffee, something he had not seen since he left Mobile a year earlier.

Less than a month later the war ended, and Atwood was among a large number of ragged Confederate soldiers who surrendered them-selves to General E.R.S. Canby, U.S.A., the Federal Provost Marshall in Jackson, Mississippi. On May 20th he received his parole (I have seen it often — Atwood has it hanging on the wall in his dressing room) and transportation by rail to Brookhaven, a small town in the southeast corner of Mississippi, still some one hundred miles from home. From there he had to make his way as best he could. It was over four weeks before he arrived in New Orleans, totally exhausted and in clothes so torn and threadbare that he said it was lucky we arrived by night because he was practically naked.

Unbeknownst to all of us, we had been traveling the same road south as Atwood, only two or so days behind him. He arrived in New Orleans just the evening before us, and he told us how he had gone by the house and, finding no one there, went in search of someone he knew to beg a meal from. He said he had become quite adept and shameless about that and soon found some friends of the family, the Prestons over on Carondelet Street, who not only fed him but gave him a bed for the night and the promise of food and lodging until his family returned. It was not until the next morning that he returned to the corner of Fourth and Prytania Streets.

In the morning light he saw the scars of three years of neglect that had been invisible the night before. In the rear of the house he found the key to the door leading to the kitchen where it had been hidden under a loose stone in the wall years before. He climbed the cast iron steps to the door and inserted it in the lock. Before he could turn the key the door gave under the pressure of his hand and swung open. A cool rush of air swept over him as he walked quietly into the house carrying with him a certain apprehension as to what he might find there.

The kitchen was filthy and the larder door off its hinges, lying on its side against the wall. He passed through into the back hallway, pausing to look into Papa's study on the left and the dining room before he ventured into the main hall. Dirt and abuse were everywhere, quite noticeable even in the dim light coming through the closed shutters. In the front hall and the parlor things were much the same, except that the parlor furniture had been badly damaged, especially the chairs, whose legs were mostly all broken off. Charred ends in the fireplace showed that they had been used for firewood.

He would not tell us what happened when he went upstairs or what he found there no matter how we begged. He just said there was some unpleasantness that we were better off not knowing about. In any event he knew that the house was empty of soldiers or other undesirables, so he set about to clean it up as best he could and had spent most of the day doing so. He was about to return to the Prestons when he heard us arriving at the front gate.

After Atwood finished his story I imagine it was twenty minutes before we thought to move from where we sat like a happy band of gypsies on our own doorstep. Finally we gathered up our belongings and trooped into the dark front hall. It felt so good to be home again that we hardly realized or cared that we had almost nothing to eat. We would finish off what little we had with us, and in the morning we could start our lives again!

Atwood had a brief word in private with Papa who came back to say that he thought it best if we "camped out" downstairs that night and waited until the morning to explore the rest of the house. We brought in everything from the carriage and Papa and Atwood took it and the horses around to the stables and fixed them up for the night. We were preparing our very modest supper in the kitchen when there was a loud knock on the front door. Fearing it might be Union soldiers, Papa shut us into the dining room before he opened the door. Behind the dining room door we strained to hear what was happening. The suspense was unbearable! Then we heard Papa say in a pleased, relieved voice, "Why Mr. Preston, what a charming surprise! Come in, come in."

Chapter 5

We emerged from the dining room like chickens from a coop and crowded round Mr. Preston, who seemed a bit startled by our sudden appearance. He put the lantern he had carried to light his way through the dark streets down on the porch floor and entered the house. He had seen us pass by on our way home and had come over to offer his assistance. His kindness brought tears to our eyes. We had not known him or his wife very well, they being older than our parents, and their three children, two boys and a girl, much older than any of our lot. We were, as the saying goes "passing acquaintances," but now he seemed the dearest, oldest friend in the world. When he heard that we had so little to eat he immediately insisted that we accompany him to his home for our evening meal. He would have offered us lodgings for the night as well, but his house was far too small for our number.

Leaving the darkie "employee" that had accompanied him to stand guard over our meagre possessions, we happily followed him to his home. It was strange to pass so many unlit houses, and the city seemed unnaturally quiet. Mr. Preston's house, though small, was brightly lit and well furnished — a welcome contrast to the empty rooms with scattered pieces of dirty, broken furniture at home.

Mrs. Preston, a short, stout, white-haired woman wearing very old-fashioned clothes, greeted us at the door as though we had been expected to dine with her all along. She had anticipated our acceptance of her husband's invitation and had had her girl prepare a hearty meal for us. I can smell that bouillabaisse right now as I am writing these words. It was just about the best meal I ever ate, garnished as it was with the consideration and concern of the Prestons. There was even some wine for the grown-ups and, as a special treat, Atwood was given a whole glass for himself. I remember the ruby color of the wine and the trembling paler red shadow on the tablecloth, projected there by the light of the candles.

We returned home filled with good food, warmed and strengthened by this unexpected hospitality and, speaking for myself, so sleepy that I remember little more than Papa's face holding a candle over us where we lay in our blankets on the parlor floor and then his receding figure tiredly walking over to where Ma lay and snuffing out the candle. It was good to fall asleep feeling your brothers and sisters close around you in the dark of your own home.

Just as the last thing that I saw the night before was Papa standing over me, the first thing I saw in the morning was Papa opening the wooden shutters of the parlor windows. Bright summer sunlight poured into the room and along with it the sounds of the city, so familiar and so long unheard — sort of a distant drone punctuated with the tinkle of far away peddlers' bells and the closer creak and crunch of wagon wheels. Occasionally a steamboat at the levee blew a warning whistle blast. Those sounds, so woven into my memory, are gone forever. New Orleans is so different now.

We rose to find that Papa had recovered some washbasins and a cracked ewer that he had filled with water from the cistern. Mr. Preston in his continuing generosity had sent over a large pot of coffee, another of hot milk and some loaves of bread. This we consumed to the last drop and crumb and then set out to explore the house and grounds.

Papa had risen early and, as I found out later, had with Atwood's help removed some mysterious object from one of the rooms on the second floor and taken it off the property. Ma had seen them returning through the gate and asked them what they were up to, but they would not tell her. I later got it from Atwood that they had taken something unpleasant away, but he would not tell me what it was or whose room it had been in. Whatever it was I think it had something to do with why the Union soldiers had cleared out.

There was litter and minor damage in all the rooms but nothing too serious. The worst part was the feeling that strangers, perhaps negro soldiers even, had used our home for God knows what purposes. The house seemed dirtier than could be cured by sweeping and washing. Some of the more valuable pieces of furniture were missing and there were few pieces left of our plates and crockery that weren't cracked or chipped. The paintings Papa had ingeniously hidden over the false ceiling of his study were safe, but badly foxed by the moisture that had accumulated in that confined space.

Papa waited until nightfall to probe the cistern with a hooked pole to recover our cache of silver. Ma couldn't understand why we had to wait and be so secretive, but Papa said there were spies about that could inform on us for half its value and in any case, you never could tell, we might have to use the hiding place again. So we waited, but it was all there, which was a great comfort.

All this, except for the silver, we accomplished before eight in the morning. Papa was in a frenzy to get to his office and find out from his partner, Mr. Black, what remained of the "wreck of his fortune," as he phrased it. Taking Atwood with him, Papa went first to a clothier, who soon had them dressed in presentable if not elegant clothes. Papa was not going to appear before his partner in the "beggar's rags" that he had arrived in from Mobile.

When he returned home in mid afternoon he was grayer and more tired looking than I had ever seen him. Clearly the news had been bad, how bad I never found out. The good news that day was that two of our servants had heard of our return and come back to us. They were Sam the stableboy and Julia the kitchenmaid. Because they had never been slaves there was no problem re-employing them on their previous terms. Ma set them to cleaning out the house with Ella, Ned, Minnie and myself as assistants. Meanwhile she and Atwood went to the market to reprovision the larder — the first part of the house she had cleaned up. We hung the mattresses over the balcony railing to air and tied what decent sheets and pillowcases we could find to an improvised clothesline after Julia had boiled them in the copper kettle back of the house.

We carried out all the trash and broken furniture and piled it in the back yard for burning. We made besom-brooms and swept and swept the house until we were ready to drop and still we found more dirt to deal with, but each time we reswept, the house seemed more our own again. We were sweeping out all reminders of those unwanted, uninvited "tenants" of the past three years. All day long we worked to bring our home back to some semblance of decency. By nightfall the beds were made, the rooms clean if empty of most furniture and rugs, and there was food in the larder. We had the essentials for existence.

Each day of the first week of our return is clear in my memory, but then the days, the weeks, even the months all blur, and I can remember only impressions of the new world that old New Orleans had become under "reconstruction" rule. When we went to sleep in our own beds for the first time in three years, I, for one, felt as though I had been holding my breath all the time that we were away. Now I could let it out and relax completely; all the stiff defenses against uncertainty collapsed.

I slept the clock around and when I awoke the sun through my window had marched across the floor to the edge of the wardrobe. (This was my own private sundial that told me the time in the morning quite accurately.) I got downstairs to find that Ella, Ned and Minnie had also overslept. Julia was just then feeding them a breakfast of milk and fresh hot rolls from the bakery and I was quick to join them. Papa had left for his office and Ma was on the veranda talking with some ladies — catching up with the news, I suppose. I bolted down my meal and left the table. I had something to do that couldn't wait a moment longer.

When I was seven years old I "inherited" a large doll house from Ella, who at eleven thought herself too old for such childish things. It had originally belonged to Grandma Oldham and was my most prized possession. I would play with it for hours. It was about three feet long and maybe eighteen inches wide, with a living room, dining room and kitchen on the first floor, and a front hall with stairs leading up to the second floor, where there were two bedrooms and a baby's room. It was the kind that opens up in the back so you can reach in and arrange the little pieces of furniture and figures. There was even access to an attic space where you could store unwanted things, just like in a real house.

Maybe that is where my love of houses started. The doors all worked and the windows opened out onto the veranda in front. (The doll house was styled after a typical Vieux Carré New Orleans house.) Wrought iron balcony railings had been carefully imitated in some sort of metal stamping, and over the front door hung a tiny lantern into which you could put tallow and a small wick. There were even miniature candles and holders inside the rooms so that with the room darkened and these tiny candles lit, the doll house seemed so real I expected the little figurines to come walking out the door.

I could go on about it forever and I don't want to bore you, but just let me describe it a little more — it's such a pleasure for me to do so. On either end of the house were chimneys of imitation brick built against the outside walls. Their flues actually opened into the fireplaces in the house. Papa would blow cigar smoke down them and you could see it come out into the rooms. "Time for a chimney sweep, Lily," he would say and laugh. Ma complained that it made the doll house smell, but I didn't mind and besides I have always liked the smell of good cigars.

Before we left New Orleans in 1862, I had persuaded Papa and Atwood to hide my doll house somewhere. They carried it out to the stable and up into the loft, where there was a pile of moldy hay that was quite useless for feed. They wrapped my precious doll house and its contents in canvas, put it on the floor in the corner and strewed some broken laths over it. On top of all this they repiled the moldy hay. All during the time that we were in Mobile I daydreamed about my doll house. I had to find out if it was still there.

I was so afraid it would be gone that I half wanted to put off looking, and it was with a pounding heart that I climbed the ladder to the loft area. Finding the hay still there, I burrowed into it in the corner where we had left the doll house. It wasn't there! I was stunned. I fled to the house wailing for Ma, who swept me up and finally calmed me so she (and all the rest of the startled family) could understand what I was saying. Ma said, "Let's look again, maybe you mistook the corner," and with me and the rest of the children, Julia and Sam trailing behind her, marched over to the stable. Despite her cumbersome dress, she managed the ladder and we attacked the pile of hay, and there in the middle of the wall was the canvas-wrapped doll house.

Now I know that that was not where we left it. Someone, looking for booty, had found it, unwrapped it and had the kindness to realize how precious it was to some child, perhaps like his own. I have a vivid picture of that unknown man in the half light of the stable loft carefully rewrapping and rehiding my doll house. Yankee or Southerner, black or white, I bless him for his humanity.

With my doll house safely re-installed in my bedroom, I felt that life had pretty much returned to normal. We bought new furniture to replace the damaged and stolen pieces and the house took back its settled look. We rehung the family pictures, even though they were a bit moldy-looking, and Papa hired a man to prune the crêpe myrtle trees at the front of the house that had grown wild during our absence. Ma said it was like living with a man that needs a haircut and a good brushing, having those trees look so scraggly. The house and the cast iron work needed painting, but Papa said it would have to wait because he couldn't spare the money.

Neighbors that had left New Orleans as we had came back, one after another, and slowly the neighborhood re-formed. Miss Cena, ever the relentless educator, got her school operating and things seemed pretty much as they had been before the war, at least to my eleven year old eyes. Except for one jarring note — the Yankee soldiers that seemed to be everywhere, especially the negro soldiers in Union uniforms. That was just the strangest thing to me; it didn't make any sense at all. I learned later that it was not just children that couldn't accept the negro soldiers — adults felt the same way only even more so.

The Confederacy had been totally defeated. Southerners accepted that. They also more or less accepted the emancipation of the negro slave, but they could not accept a social order that granted the negroes social, political or any other form of equality with whites. When it came to being ordered around by negroes in Yankee uniforms, or having laws passed by a legislature that was largely composed of negroes and Northerners, or even having negroes in local administrative positions, Southerners were ready to do battle again, and it wasn't long before it actually came to that.

Papa asked Atwood what he wanted to do — go back to college to finish his education or go into business with him. Without hesitation Atwood chose to go in with Papa. He told me much later that if he had realized the extra burden he was putting on Papa he might have chosen otherwise, but the business education that he got was invaluable. Papa spent hours each day with Atwood teaching him as much as he could. Even at night after dinner, he would have Atwood working on the firm's accounts in his study. Atwood learned quickly. With his natural aptitude for business and great desire to please his adored father, he soon became more help than hindrance.

It was most peculiar, but the winter of 1865–66 saw as many, if not more, large social affairs as were held during the last season before the war. People really didn't have the money for entertaining and there certainly was nothing to celebrate, but nevertheless there was at least one ball or fête each week. I think now that there were two reasons for this. These parties were "exclusive" affairs in the truest form of the word. Neither Union officers and their wives nor negroes of any rank or elevation in the new order were ever invited. The parties gave us a chance to regroup, to reassure each other of our capabilities, and to forget for a moment the humiliations that were daily heaped upon us in the outside world. Secondly, by excluding them, we took a petty but very real revenge on the Union officers, the carpetbaggers and all the rest of our tormentors from the North. They, who were so insensitive toward us in so many ways, were peculiarly sensitive to these social snubs. They, and especially their wives, could not comprehend such treatment, and it gave us malicious satisfaction to be able to strike back at them so successfully.

There was also a message to the colored population from these parties. We were saying, "Don't let this emancipation and all that make you think that anything has really changed between whites and negroes. That's still just the same."

Chapter 6

Papa got his pardon from President Johnson in November of 1865 and was able to regain about one half of his business properties that had been confiscated. The rest were either gone, or so tied up with claims and counterclaims that Papa said they were as good as gone. I'm sure it was very hard for him to accept this great price he had to pay for his part in the war that he had tried so hard to prevent, but he never mentioned it. When it came to complaining Papa was silence personified. Sometimes I think that things would have been better in some areas if he had spoken his mind more freely.

The next few years, 1866, '67 and '68 are such a muddle in my mind that I don't know if I can give you an accurate impression of them, but I will do the best I can.

First, Ella was sixteen, a real beauty (if a little on the prim side) and looking forward to her imminent début into New Orleans society. During our exile in Mobile she was sure that the war would go on forever and she would get older and older and never have a chance to be a "belle." Now we were re-established in New Orleans and her début was only eighteen months away. She planned and talked of nothing else.

But it was not the same New Orleans as before the war in any way but physically. There was so much violence on the streets that it was very hard to go about doing the normal day-to-day activities, and the social battle going on between New Orleans society and the occupying Federal troops was almost as intense as a war itself. The air fairly crackled with bad feeling in high society and in low.

Then, too, something began to happen between Ma and Papa — something never spoken of, but apparent and unpleasant. Their conversations seemed a bit strained and unnatural; there was little of their former good-natured banter. Papa was engaged in a terrible struggle to regain complete control of his business assets and to avoid the confiscatory penalties that were being imposed on businessmen in the form of "costs" incurred in the formalities of deeding back to them their own businesses and properties. It was a frustrating, demeaning, endless process and Papa was naturally nervous and irritable.

Finally in the winter of 1867, Papa said that some recent and particularly nasty happenings between whites and blacks had convinced him that we were no longer safe in New Orleans, so he was sending us to stay in Toronto, Canada, until order was restored in the South. "Toronto!" we cried. "Why in Heaven's name do we have to go to Toronto and just exactly where is it anyway? Why can't we go and stay with Aunt Catherine in Louisville or with the Oldhams in Cincinnati or the Martins in Pittsburgh?"

"Because," he replied, "there's too much bad feeling in those cities against Southerners; it wouldn't be fair to burden our relations there. Many Southerners have already sent their families to Toronto and you will feel more at home among them. It is not a very civilized city compared to New Orleans, but the people are pleasant and very sympathetic to us. I've been there several times on business and although the weather can be quite chilly in the winter, I'm sure you'll get used to it. Besides, you'd be going away this coming summer in any case, so it is only an extra few months."

The rest of us accepted our fate; after all we were well accustomed to travel, especially during the last three years, but Ella absolutely refused to go. How could she come out in New Orleans society when she was tucked away in the wilds of Canada? When she got back, if she ever did, all her friends would have had their presentation ball and met and married the few eligible beaux that had survived the war. If she left now her life would be ruined, she would probably never marry and would become a sourpuss old maid!

Papa was inflexible and said she must go, it was for her own good and he would hear no more about the matter, and of course in those days, a father's word was law. He promised there would be plenty of parties and lots of young men (from good families he was sure), and Ella would have a gay old time indeed. I remember that Ma was strangely silent and unprotesting during all this argument, considering how much she had been looking forward to Ella's début.

Two weeks later, toward the end of January, we left for the North. As the weather was mild the steamboat was able to take us up river as far as Cincinnati, where, after a brief stay with the Oldhams, we switched to railroad transportation. During that week in Cincinnati I came to realize for the first time exactly why we couldn't stay there for any length of time. Our Northern cousins and uncles had been in the Union Army; I saw the pictures of them in uniform on the walls. They had actually fought against us, shot and killed people we probably knew, and had been shot at and seen their friends and kin killed by our soldiers. It had just never occurred to me before that the war had been that personal. Before I had thought that the Yankees we fought were everyone else except our relatives. It had never penetrated my mind that they had been as involved in the Northern cause as we were in the Southern one.

Hard as it was to accept this, it was a fact of life, and when it came time to leave I was glad to go. The Oldhams had done the best they could, but their hospitality was forced. Even we children could feel it and I am sure they were just as glad to see us go.

Nevertheless, after we boarded the train and waved goodbye to the Oldhams, we were on our own, traveling into the "frozen North" as Ella grimly put it, leaving everything familiar behind us. We had never been north in winter before, and from the warm comfort of the train the snow-covered trees and frozen lakes were excitingly different. Childlike, we didn't think ahead to the time when we should leave the train and experience those frigid temperatures on our inadequately clothed bodies. We found out with a vengeance upon our arrival in Cleveland the next day. The shock was so great that Ma decided to stay in a hotel there for a few days so that we could remedy the thermal deficiencies of our New Orleans clothes with warmer, if less fashionable, garments. It was a fine hotel, the "Lakeshore," I believe, and we enjoyed our stopover immensely. If this was what Toronto was going to be like we would be quite content.

Unfortunately, such was not the case. When the steamboat from Buffalo deposited our half frozen bodies on Maitland's Wharf at the juncture of Front and Church Streets in Toronto, what we saw seemed more a frontier town than a city. From the deck of the ferry as it tied up we could see the entire breadth of the "city" — from the domed lunatic asylum in the west to the cruciform city gaol in the east. Never was a city more symbolically bounded. After we had been there but a short time it was very clear how easily one might be driven to crime or insanity.

Fortunately our hotel, the "Wellington," though just across Front Street, had sent a convenience to fetch us and our baggage, or we never could have made the short trip through the drifting snow and gusting, frigid winds that caught and tugged at our voluminous clothing. Even so, Minnie was blown down when she came off the gangway, and Ma gave a frightened scream as she snatched her away from the wharf's edge.

The Hotel Wellington was about the same age as its namesake and probably in about the same physical condition — that is, as we used to say, "Dead or no difference." The rooms on the first floor were warm enough to prevent shivering, but just barely so. The fires had been laid for economy and gave off only a grudging show of heat. Our rooms on the second floor faced the lake, giving us a good view and a bad breeze that rattled the windows and sent gusts right through the heavy draperies that we pulled across them, so they billowed out like a woman's skirt when she turns suddenly.

If the accommodations were poor, the food was appallingly worse. Roast beef boiled and then baked so that all the juices were first leached out and then the result dried in the oven to the consistency of mud brown cardboard. Vegetables were treated in a similiar fashion so that carrots and peas had the same taste and consistency and potatoes were mashed to a porridge-like mess. All these swam in a glutinous brown gravy and this collage was our unvarying dinner fare. We, who had traveled widely before the war, had always considered all other cooking a poor second to that of New Orleans, but never had we encountered anything as bad as what we endured in Toronto.

To complete our misery the incredible cold kept us prisoners indoors except for short dashes to the St. Lawrence Market two blocks away on Front Street and to St. Andrew's Church a half mile up Church Street. There was, as promised, a small colony of Southerners, who, like ourselves, were refugees from the violence of reconstruction. We children

69

played with our counterparts when the weather permitted, but the long gray days between these outings were indescribably boring. Even irrepressible Minnie ran out of ideas to amuse us. We read and sewed and did our homework two times over. (There was a local school that we attended each morning for three hours.) We took our meals in the dreary dining room and retired to our icy bedrooms only for sleep.

The only thing that saved us from commitment to that asylum west of town was the piano in the main parlor and a lady called Madame Arnaut, a refugee from a plantation near Baton Rouge that had been destroyed by the Yankees. Her husband, like Papa, was trying to rebuild his fortunes and had sent her and her older spinster sister to Toronto to be out of harm's way. She had lost both her sons during the war and was in a very melancholy state, spending hours sitting in the parlor, gazing with softly focused eyes out the window, as if she hoped to see some special person coming to the front door.

Minnie had a little competence with the piano and would amuse herself with it, playing and singing little pieces she had learned at home. It turned out that Madame Arnaut had studied voice in Paris during her youth, and soon she was passing her knowledge on to Minnie. They became close, and I believe she had a great deal to do with Minnie's development as a fine operatic singer. Every afternoon she would have Minnie doing exercises and practicing simple arias from some of the musical scores that she had with her. We would come in and listen and Madame would teach us little pieces to play and sing, but just for fun. She had recognized that Minnie had a real talent and was fascinated to see it develop.

So the winter dragged on and on until finally spring came and things got better. We got out more, the townspeople seemed more friendly, we were invited to a number of parties, and Ella went to a dance at the St. Lawrence Hall. Ma, too, socialized a bit more, but she was very reserved and unapproachable to the males present at these gatherings. She was desperately lonely for Papa and more than a bit hurt by being shunted off to that dreary town.

Ma was forty-two that year and still a very handsome woman. She was, I think, completely in love with Papa, but I fear she did not trust him to be as true to her as she would like. As I found out later, she was suspicious at the time that Papa might be involved with someone else, but she said nothing about it to us then, of course. I don't think she said anything specific to Papa either, hoping I suppose that anything that was going on would run its course and die without her having to have an ugly confrontation with him. Poor Ma; poor Papa too, I guess. He was much too moral a man to enter into any such situation lightly.

Chapter 7

Atwood Violett
33 West 51st Street
New York City

September 22, 1925

Dear Mally,

Atwood, Olga, the children and I are back in New York and I am about to pick up my writing where I left off in July, but I find on reading the last few pages about Toronto that I am in a bit of a quandary.

When Ma died at Atlantic City in 1908, I was with her. A few days before the end, she asked me to bring her the small blue velvet box with the brass studding that she used to hold her little treasures. From it she removed one thing and another, laying them on the bed beside her. Near the bottom she found a stack of letters tied together with a faded purple ribbon which she removed. With trembling hands she selected a letter, handed it to me, and asked me to read it.

Oh, how I remember that moment! It was in the early afternoon of a warm June day. The blinds were drawn down to the tops of the open windows and a light breeze crept past the white muslin curtains into the darkened room where Ma lay on the bed with a light blanket over her thin legs, propped up on some pillows so she could breathe easier. She looked so frail and old, but I could still see the lovely young woman that I had known when I was young myself.

From outside came the faint sounds of ocean waves and the sandy crunching of feet on the boardwalk as I carefully unfolded the thin worn letter.

It was in Ma's distinctive hand, that small, barely punctuated scrawl, seldom capitalized at the beginning of sentences, so hard for the uninitiated to decipher. The letter was dated Toronto, March 12, 1867, and even though it is quite long I am going to quote it all because it is so eloquent about Ma's feelings and situation at the time. (I have added punctuation and capital letters where needed.) She wrote:

My Dear Husband,

Yours of the 22nd reached me last night. I thank you kindly, for your good long letter and the complimentary manner in which you speak of me. I feel that I am quite undeserving of all these flattering encomiums.

Since I wrote last I have quite recovered. I walked out yesterday and felt much better after enjoying the cool bracing air. I have never been as sick since I had the Fever. The Doctor says his prompt treatment prevented me having a serious spell. My appetite is so delicate and the fare so abominable, that is, it is so badly cooked, I could not eat anything. There are no ladies' restaurants here where you can get anything. I went to a confectionary and begged the woman to get me something I could eat. She sent out and got me some oysters and made a nice oyster soup and gave me a good cup of coffee as well. I enjoyed it very much.

Ella has been home for several days, sick & quite bilious. The Dr. gave her blue mass and oil. She is much better today & will go to school tomorrow. The rest are well. Mr. Thompson has not treated Lily for some time. He is not here now and Dr. Blackburn makes me put wet bandages around her legs. She keeps them on all day, but she looks the picture of health and has a good appetite. [Oh, how I remember those hated bandages!] She and Minnie are studying very hard; they want to surprise you when you come. Poor Ned, I am afraid he will never improve; he is so slow in learning.

The weather has been spring-like for some days past, but has changed since last night. It is now snowing quite hard. Everything is covered with a downy mantle. Sleighing has commenced again. I have been on the lookout for a house for

the summer, both here and in St. Catherines. I wrote to two
ladies there about a house and one, a Mrs. McDonald, wrote
me back last night. I think I had better go over there and
make some arrangement for the summer. I can get private
board, but it would not be so pleasant. I know of several
houses here for rent, but none furnished though I understand
you can hire furniture here by the month. A Mr. Charles
Ross's house is for rent and I am going up with Mr. Joseph
this afternoon to see it and will write you full particulars. I
sent for young Dahlgren to come and see me but I suppose he
is too diffident to call.

Until the summer I would like very much to board with
Capt. Thorenson at the Stephenson House. He knows how to
keep a hotel far better than the owners of the Wellington.

All of the Southerners here are going to Niagara Town, but
I do not like that place. It feels like a graveyard it is so quiet. I
suppose it would be too expensive to board at the Stephenson
House.

I am so glad sister Emma is coming on. It will benefit her
health no doubt. I think Emma is perfectly right about the
Waynes. They will compromise our position in Society. Do
you suppose Mollie's midnight brawl is erased from the
minds of those that witnessed it? She made a very plausible
story of it, but had she been a woman of refinement and
delicacy she never would have placed herself in that position.
If my poor sister was out of the set I would not care if I never
saw any of them again. They have been the means of keeping
me from my home. In January you urged upon me the
necessity of remaining here since the Waynes would compromise my position if I returned and it was mostly in consideration of this than anything else I concluded to remain, but I
will not stay here in Toronto past next September, no matter
what.

I received a letter from Mrs. Tate lately. Said she received a
letter from Mr. Harrod. He said his family had seen "Mrs.
Violett" and she was well. Wanted to know if I was in Canada
or New Orleans. I suppose they saw Mollie with you and

took her for me. She must appreciate your attentions very much.

I have felt so miserably homesick for the past few days. I try not to feel unhappy. You speak of the possibility of my having to remain in Canada. Nothing will induce me to consent to this. This separation from you and Atwood has cost me enough pain already. I will go home and live in two rooms before I submit to it. If I was like some women here I might find solace in the society of other gentlemen. Plenty of opportunities.

[Here, several lines of the letter are heavily crossed out.]

Why is it Ma does not write to me? I have only received one in three months from her. Poor Ma, what a life she leads. I hope sister O. has recovered. You did not mention Atwood once in your long letter. I hope he is well. Give much love to him.

I have not received the draft yet. I am still unable to pay my debts. It makes me feel so unpleasantly. I am looking out for an Italian teacher for Ella. Dr. B. wrote you last night. I am so glad to hear you have recovered. Do take good care of yourself my dear husband, how I long to embrace you and my dear Atwood. Have you no idea when you can come up to Canada? I hope business is better, your last letter was not too encouraging on that score. I did not send the Ferrotypes. They are not good. I will send some of mine soon. Give Emma & Mrs. Insley one each. Did you tell Mrs. Insley I wrote to her? Give much love to her & also to Ma and sister. I hope to receive a good long letter soon from you.

Your devoted and loving wife,
Nel

P.S. Ella had her likeness taken for some of the girls. I did not know she intended having them so small. She sends one to Emma. Tell Atwood I will write in a few days. Children all send love to dear Papa and Atwood. Mary sends much love.

Nel

My dilemma is that as I said before and as you may have inferred from the letter Papa was involved with another woman and I don't know whether I should tell what I know about it or not. Rather, I don't know whether it should go in the memoirs for the family to read. I will tell you about it in this letter and let you decide how much of it to keep in the record.

You will notice that there are several lines crossed out in the middle of the letter. I did that at Ma's request that afternoon in her room at Atlantic City. In those lines Ma had made some remarks to Papa that she felt were unjust, and she didn't want them to be seen by strangers. I asked her why she hadn't destroyed the whole letter, but she said that she thought it had some meaning and we children could learn something from it. I frankly don't know what she meant, but I have kept the letter all these years and now I am glad I did — it recalls so vividly our dismal time in Canada.

When I returned the letter to her, she took my hand and told me the story that she had kept to herself for forty years. It didn't come out too coherently, but in short this is what she told me.

The woman's first name was Mollie (there is no point in giving out her last name), and she was the widow of one of the officers in the Violett Guards, the company that Papa had organized and financed at the beginning of the war. Her husband was a handsome but improvident sort and when he was killed at Shiloh, he left her penniless with two very young children to raise. Furthermore, due to the misfortunes of war there was no family of her own or of his that she could appeal to for help. Knowing that Papa had supported the families of the foot soldiers in his company until New Orleans fell, she approached him with her problem after our return to the city in 1865.

She was about seven or eight years younger than Ma, not beautiful but quite pretty in a gamine way. Her husband had been of our class, but she was of slightly lesser social stature. She had exhausted the hospitality of her friends and was desperate as to her next move. Papa was appalled by her plight and that night talked over with Ma what they should do to help. With her approval, Papa established Mollie in a little house just north of the French Quarter and gave her a small allowance to live on. From time to time he would visit with her on his way home from the Cotton Exchange, and occasionally she would be a guest in our house.

After a year or so Papa's visits became more frequent than paternal interest would excuse, but Ma knew nothing of that then, she only felt an increasing distance between herself and Papa — a wall where there had been openness before. When Papa began to sponsor Mollie for inclusion in the social circle of their friends, Ma began to sense the source of her difficulties.

This must have been in the fall of 1866, just before his decision to send us to Toronto "to get us out of harm's way," as he put it at the time.

I honestly don't think that Papa had an actual "affaire" with Mollie; I think he was terribly fond of her and found in her company something important to him that Ma could not give him. As I said before, he was a very honest, moral person with a great sense of his family responsibilities, so it must have been a powerful emotion that he felt to make him wander even so slightly from the straight and narrow path.

I hope that I am not shocking you too much by this story of your great grandfather's "affaire." You must remember that social customs in New Orleans were almost totally European then. Many prominent men kept quadroon mistresses quite openly, had children by them, sent the boys to France for their education, and provided for them in their wills. Papa's relationship with Mollie was almost totally innocent compared to the accepted customs of the town, but it was so out of keeping with his usual habits that it must have been all the more distressing to Ma.

As I learned much later, it appears that in the summer of 1867, while we were still in Toronto,* Mollie came to the attention of a Mr. "X," a widower some ten or more years younger than Papa and what we called a "Scalawag," that is to say a Southerner who cooperated with the minions of the Federal Government for his own financial benefit. Papa knew of him by reputation and deeply resented his paying court to Mollie. It is not known what Mollie's feelings were, but apparently she did not expressly discourage his visits to her home. When Papa went to visit Mollie, he would never know if he would find "X" there, and if he did Papa would not stay. There were scenes and violent quarrels

* *Author's note:* Penelope prevailed in her demand to return to New Orleans and arrived there with her children in the fall of 1867.

between Papa and "X" until the spring of 1868, when they fought a duel with pistols and Papa was mortally wounded.

Again you must understand that this was New Orleans, where such things were commonplace. Now, of course, duels sound faintly ridiculous, but in those days many a duel was fought with swords or pistols, and many a life was spilled on the ground under the famous Dueling Oaks out in City Park. In fact I remember reading in the paper that on one Sunday in 1839 ten duels were fought there.

There were two lofty oaks standing alone in the great expanse of the park some hundred feet from each other. Each party and his seconds would select one tree as a base of operations and from there advance to a point halfway between the two, and there the duel would be fought. Afterwards, if there was no fatality or serious wound, both parties would repair to the café at the edge of the park to take a glass or two of wine with their seconds. In Papa's case there were no glasses raised.

His friends brought him home and with muttered explanations we could not understand carried him up to his bedroom. Atwood had been sent for and came at once, pale as a sheet. He ran past us children clustered at the foot of the stairs and bounded up them two at a time. We could hear him enter and Papa's feeble, glad cry of greeting. Then the door closed and we were left alone with our fear.

Dr. Constant came, went up and into the bedroom and sent for hot water and clean sheeting. Ella, Minnie, Ned and I stood below and waited and waited. It seemed forever before the bedroom door opened and the doctor and Ma emerged. She beckoned to us and suddenly I didn't want to go up. I just knew whatever had happened to Papa it was very, very bad and I didn't want to face it. Maybe if I didn't go up it wouldn't happen. But I couldn't not go up either, so I reluctantly followed the rest. Ma didn't say a word, but she didn't have to. Her expression told Ella and me how very bad it was. Ella was quiet, but her lower lip was trembling; Ned and Minnie were docile and uncomprehending as we stood beside the bed looking at our dying father. I felt as though I were a thousand miles away from my body, completely detached, as through my eyes, like distant windows, I regarded the motionless, silent form in the bed, the shell of the vibrant, vigorous, loving man that had been my father.

Suddenly, just as I didn't want to go up those stairs then, now I just can't recount to you the details of the next few days. They are simply too painful to relive. Already I have reopened the wound too far. Suffice it to say that two days later dear Papa died, peacefully and without much pain, thank God.

Well, Mally, that's what happened. You can withhold this letter from the rest if you think it best, but I wanted you, at least, to know the truth. Incidentally, I never knew about the duel or Mollie until Ma told me in Atlantic City just before she died. At the time, we children were told that Papa had been shot in one of the innumerable street skirmishes that occurred in New Orleans during reconstruction days. Ma was too embarrassed to allow us to know the truth then.

After Papa's death Mollie "took up" with Mr. "X" and disappeared with him into the lower reaches of New Orleans society. I saw her once, years later, walking past the window of a shop that I was in. I didn't recognize her at the time, she was so changed, but something about her rang a bell in my memory and later on I realized who she was.

Well, write me and let me know what you think. In the meantime I'll go on with my story from after Papa's death.

Much love as always,
Aunt Lily

Chapter 8

When Papa died, Atwood was twenty-one, Ella was eighteen, I was fourteen, Ned was twelve, Minnie was eleven and Ma was forty-three. At first she was completely at a loss as to how to carry on alone, so Atwood stepped in and made all the decisions. He was wonderful. Thank God for Papa's foresight in training him in his business, or we would have had a very difficult time dealing with Papa's business affairs.

It turned out that before his death Papa had managed to recoup a good portion of the losses he had incurred during the war, so that we found ourselves in pretty fair financial order. Atwood made an arrangement with Papa's partner, Mr. Black, to liquidate Papa's interest in the firm. Out of the sum realized Atwood took his inheritance share and reinvested it in a new partnership with Mr. Black on quite advantageous terms because it permitted the firm to continue to use the prestigious name of Violett.

The major problem at home was Ella, who was to have been presented to New Orleans society in the 1868–69 season and would now have to wait until a decent period of mourning had elapsed. Ella was crushed by this delay, and there was much futile crying and periods of long moody silences. "I know it's very sad about Papa dying and I loved him very much, but I don't see why I have to miss out on my one big chance in life to be a belle and get married and everything. Going to Toronto put me way behind everyone else; this is just going to finish me off completely! Life isn't supposed to work out this way!"

Ella was not presented that year and it twisted her somehow. She was just as pretty as ever, but there was a hardness to her mouth and a defiance in her bearing that gave her whole appearance a slightly discordant rigidity.

A year went by — a dark and dreary year that was no better at its end than at its beginning and promised nothing but countless repetitions of itself. Sporadic incidents of violence in the city kept everyone on edge and the whole South expected the negroes to go on a general rampage at any time. There were plenty of irresponsible Yankees egging them on and you could feel the tension building up, like watching the level of the Mississippi slowly rising up the side of the levee in the springtime and wondering how high it would get.

We went north in the summer of 1869 to try and make up with our relations in Louisville and Cincinnati. Although it was a little better than our disastrous visit during the winter of 1867, it was so sad to find that the terrible chasm of the war was still between us and our cousins that we had played with so happily before the war, inhibiting all our efforts to recapture our old camaraderie.

We finally made some sort of an excuse and spent the last three weeks of our trip at a lovely new resort hotel in western Pennsylvania. It was a relief not to have to force ourselves to be congenial any longer.

Home again in New Orleans in the fall of 1869, we suffered under an unending avalanche of reconstruction horrors. News of the failure of plantation after plantation came in weekly. With no help to run them and no way to pay help if they could find it, all the grand families of the South seemed to be plunged into ruin. The lovely old mansions, the "great houses" as the colored folk called them, once so immaculate, were beginning their slow slide into the moldering ruins that they are today. Their owners, habituated since childhood to total service, now had to serve themselves. Accustomed to the finest foods and wines and clothing, they now made do with common fare and patched clothes. They were mostly gallant and uncomplaining, but oh, how far they had fallen!

By way of illustration, there was a family named Durande that Papa and Ma knew quite well, who had a magnificent plantation over by St. Martinsville called "Pine Alley." Mr. Durande and Papa had become friends through their mutual membership in the Society of the Cincinnati, an association composed of descendants of officers who had fought in the American Revolution. Charles Durande, already a wealthy man, had come to Louisiana about 1820 and bought several thousand acres of land fronting on the Bayou Teche. In a short time he had pyramided his wealth in sugar and built Pine Alley, so called for the three-mile alley of oaks and pines that led from the bayou to the main house. This large, veranda-girded mansion was furnished and appointed like a not so miniature Versailles with such refinements as gold- and silver-plated doorknobs and key guards, a bathtub carved from a single block of marble, and a king's ransom's worth of European furniture.

In 1850, about four years after their marriage, Ma and Papa were invited to attend a wedding celebration at Pine Alley for the simultaneous marriage of two of Durande's daughters. (He had twenty-four children by two wives, incidentally — twelve by the first, and then, as he used to say "to be fair" — twelve more by the second.)

For this great occasion Durande made special preparations. He imported a supply of large, web-spinning spiders from China that were set free in the oak alley several days before the double wedding, where they immediately spun hundreds of huge webs in the interlacing branches. Early on the morning of the wedding the slaves were given bellows and bags of gold or silver dust with which they sprayed the dew-laden webs so that when the guests arrived the whole arcade of trees glittered and shimmered in the sunlight as the gentle morning breeze stirred the gilt and silvered webs.

Rich oriental rugs and carpeting were spread between the trees. The minister and his acolytes stood at the end of the alley in front of an altar banked with flowers, with a thousand guests in all their finery ranged on either side of the avenue. The two brides-to-be, their proud father between them and their attendants behind, paraded down the center under that fantastic glittering web of a cathedral nave. What a sight that must have been! It was a high point of extravagance in a period that was not easily impressed, and Ma talked about it for the rest of her life.

All Durande's wealth was swept away by the war. His slaves disappeared, his mansion was stripped, his crops went unplanted, and he died a broken man in 1867. Papa, who was his friend, wept for him, that he should have been brought so low. Over the next decade or two his family scattered, and the mansion and its outbuildings were abandoned and gradually succumbed to the elements. Now, I am told, nothing remains but the alley of trees, still a magnificent cathedral nave of interwoven branches and Spanish moss, leading from nowhere to nowhere.

Hundreds of similiar stories came to us to add to our depression. Crop failures, financial ruin, and deaths, oh so many deaths — from lingering war wounds, from disease or from just plain despair. The old people especially seemed to just give up and one morning they would be found dead in their beds. Suicide was less of an occurrence than the circumstances might have warranted, but there were enough cases so that one lived in expectation of the news that another poor soul could stand the torment no longer.

With Papa gone it was very hard for us to keep our own spirits up. He was so good at times like that. Atwood was doing well in his business affairs, but he had little patience with the growing gloom at home.

Then, one night just before what promised to be another cheerless Christmas, Ma gathered us all into Papa's study and proposed that she would take us girls abroad and travel through the capitals and watering spots of Europe for the next two years. Ned would stay in New Orleans with Atwood, who would supervise his activities. We were naturally struck dumb at this totally unanticipated proposal, but when we stopped to think, it made such good sense. Like many Southerners, we had relatives in both England and France who were well connected and could see that we were introduced to the right people and invited to the important social events. Ma was sure that Ella would meet a rich, handsome, titled European who would sweep her off her feet, and that Ella's marriage would provide Minnie and me with such glamorous associations as to assure our futures as well.

At worst we would be away from the South and all the depressing troubles that we could not alleviate, only endure. Besides, so many of the South's young men had emigrated abroad to pursue professions not available at home that we would see more eligible Southerners there than anywhere in the South. (It's really incredible to me how many people emigrated. I was not aware of it at the time, but I have read since of colonies of Southern plantation owners in Brazil, Argentina, Mexico, and in Cuba and other Caribbean islands. Then too, whole families went back to England and France, back to where their antecedents had lived before they decided to emigrate to America. They have never come back, and this country lost some very fine citizens.)

Travel in those days was cheap, especially in Europe, and Atwood made no objection to Ma's proposal — in fact he was all for it. I am sure he was sincere in his belief that the change of scenery would do us all a world of good, but I am equally sure that he was glad to get us out of the house. We were not the best of company, and we were a worry to him because he was always concerned for our physical safety when we went about the city.

Ella was entranced with the idea. It was simply incredible to see the instant change it made in her physical appearance as well as her spirits; she was like a parched flower that suddenly feels the rain. She entered into a whirlwind of activity, brushing up on her Italian, refining her French idiom to conform to European usages, planning wardrobes, and poring over every book on Europe that she could find. Minnie and I were only fractionally less excited.

Gradually our plans took shape, and finally in the spring of 1870 we left New Orleans by train journeying to New York where we spent a happy week completing our wardrobes and visiting with family friends. Papa's brother Robert Gray Violett came up from Washington to see us off and gave us letters of introduction to friends of his in London, Paris, Rome and Venice. We went with him to Brooklyn where we saw a performance of Mr. Barnum's circus extravaganza billed as "The Greatest Show on Earth." It was marvelously exciting with all the lions, tigers and elephants, and on the way back Uncle pointed out the great stone piers for the new Brooklyn bridge that was being built to link that city to New York.

Finally Ma was satisfied that we were properly supplied with appropriate clothing for all possible contingencies, and we were able to relax from the countless fittings and refittings and apply our energies to supervising the packing of these literal mountains of clothing.

On the subject of clothing, it must be awesome today for modern travelers to contemplate the amount of luggage that had to be dealt with by sweating porters in those days. A knight in armor was less encumbered than we were. Just one lady's costume would fill a large modern suitcase, and often two or three changes of costume were required each day. In addition to body clothing, there were enormous hats, parasols, umbrellas and other paraphernalia. Instead of the relatively small steamer trunks that you have now — those ingenious affairs combining a miniature chest of drawers with a small closet and a shoe box underneath — we had gargantuan trunks, huge portmanteaux, hat boxes, etc. The bulk and weight of baggage per person were phenomenal.

The logistics of the disposal of this impedimenta was also monumental. For instance, on arrival at one's hotel all the trunks, cases, hat boxes, toiletry cases etc. . . . were manhandled up to the lady's room, where they were unpacked. Of course there was absolutely no room to leave them there, so they must all be taken down to the cellar until the time of departure, when the whole procedure was repeated.

All that clothing required an army of cleaners, pressers, and seamstresses for its maintenance, so that between them and the porters a lot of jobs were created for the local residents.

The physical demands on the wearer of this clothing were also considerable. One costume meant half a dozen layers of under- and overgarments: bodice, bustle, overskirt and underskirt, chemise and petticoat, each with a score of tiny buttons to be fitted into almost invisible and fragile loops, many of which were located in places practically impossible for the wearer to reach. Then there was the famous, formidable whaleboned corset to draw in the waist, push out the bosom, and incidentally make it quite impossible for the wearer to take even a reasonably deep breath. Since these corsets could not be unlaced without the help of another person, many a woman fainted away before her lungs could be released. The cry "give her air," never heard today, was quite literally true then.

In addition were the stockings, the high-button shoes, the many-buttoned gloves, the hat to be carefully attached with pins to the elaborately coiffured hair, and the parasol to be carried to protect one from the sun. And if the weather changed while one was preparing for an outdoor affair, the whole process had to be undone and then gone through again. It was an exhausting procedure.

We sailed from Hoboken, New Jersey, on a raw, windy day in March of 1870 on the "Oceanic," the newest ship of the White Star Line on the transatlantic run. She was 420 feet long with a crew of 150 and could accommodate 311 passengers. She was bigger than anything we had ever seen on the Mississippi and as beautifully appointed as a fine hotel. Where earlier passenger ships had the lounges and cabins in small wooden deckhouses, these were were built right into the hull of the ship and were extremely well lighted and ventilated. Instead of massive sidewheels, the Oceanic had a single large "screw" propellor at the stern. She still had sails though; engines were not reliable enough then to be the only means of propulsion. It was a lovely combination, and I was sad to see the sails done away with in the newer ships we used on later trips abroad.

Our appreciation of the ship's "architecture" was short-lived. Despite the Oceanic's great size, the long gray rollers of the Atlantic reduced us to sodden lumps of misery for the next two days. None of our many trips on the Mississippi had prepared us for the awful effects of seasickness. Then all was well again, and the rest of the voyage was passed pleasantly. The weather became quite balmy, the sea flattened out and the huge propellor, with assistance from the sails, pushed us along at a tremendous speed.

The Southampton dock reminded us of a bigger, dirtier, colder form of the New Orleans levee, but London itself was everything that our reading of Dickens had led us to expect and more. Our hotel, the Connaught, was so different though — nothing like the hotels we were used to in America. The lobby was like a large parlor in a private home with sofas and deep chairs and waiters serving tea. The beds in our rooms were waist-high, with little steps next to them to make the ascent easier. The smell of coal smoke that came through the window was harsh at first, but soon became unnoticeable. (Although now whenever I think of London that is the first thing that comes to mind.)

We were met on arrival by Ma's cousin Alfred Martin, who came originally from Cincinnati, but had gone to Washington before the war to work in the Department of State. After the war, he accepted a post in the diplomatic corps and was stationed at our London embassy. He was five years older than Ma — so he would have been forty-eight at the time, a tall, burly man with a florid complexion who towered over his short, plump wife, Emma. She had a pretty face, framed in the most beautiful honey blond hair I have ever seen. English, from a distinguished family, she was very straightforward and a more agreeable, easy person to be with would be hard to find. No one could have been better qualified than the Martins to ensure our comforts and our introduction into London society.

We found that we were far from the only Southern Belles that had journeyed across the waters in search of peace and possibly a husband. There were quite a few in town, but we were all so popular that there were plenty of gentlemen to go around. They loved our "accent" and thought we were all experts on every detail of the war, which they were most interested in. In short, we were besieged with invitations to dinners, luncheons, the opera, and the theatre. Unfortunately for me and for Minnie there were many of these occasions that we, being only sixteen and twelve, were ineligible to attend, but our vicarious pleasure in Ella and Ma's participation swept us along with them in our imagination.

During the day, when we were not shopping or otherwise engaged, we saw all the great sights of London. It was all so new and yet so familiar at the same time. I had the strange feeling that I had seen it all before in some dream. The Tower of London, Buckingham Palace, Westminster Abbey, and the Houses of Parliament seemed like comfortable old acquaintances that you have not seen for a long time. The poignancy of the little marble effigies of the long-dead children of one of the kings, I forget which, moved me greatly. Those barren rooms in the Tower where so many great Englishmen spent their last hours — I could see them and feel their despair. When I looked at the block and saw the executioner's axe, I could sense an anticipatory tingle at the nape of my neck, a small echo of Anne Boleyn's experience.

In mid May we went down into Kent and saw the Cathedral at Canterbury and then traveled west through the lovely English countryside. Lofty silver-gray beech trees whose branches twined together overhead scattered the soft May sunlight into a thousand fragments, and the high verges on either side of the road were deep green with moss, still wet from winter snows. Birds sang their greetings to us, and the hills in the distance were hazy green with the promise of summer yet to come. The little villages we passed through sparkled under coats of new paint. How different it all was from the dusty heat and dilapidation of the defeated South. The change made us slightly hysterical with happiness just to be there, away from all our troubles.

Then there were the castles! If I love houses I love castles ten times more. Everything about them speaks to me of their weighty history. Mentally I rebuild the Great Hall, re-roof the stables that lie against the outer wall, replace the glass in the high, narrow chapel window and the larger window of the "solar," and people the whole with leisurely lords and ladies, scuttling varlets and minions, and all the classes in between. I feel the heat from a roaring blaze in the now cold and empty fireplaces. I see the heavy tapestries swelling and retreating from the winter drafts they endeavor to restrain. I imagine the damp coolness that would lie behind those massive stone walls on a hot summer day when the fields outside would shimmer whitely in the sun, or how the checkered countryside would look from the top of the inner bailey on a wet March morning with fat, cold raindrops dripping off the leafless trees. In these surroundings all the great historical figures of medieval English history are reincarnated to replay their lives for me.

During that spring and summer we made many excursions into southern England and always managed to include a "castle tour." There was Bodiam Castle in Kent — a perfect little jewel lying in the middle of a small artificial lake in which swam three huge swans, their necks curved in the shape of large white question marks. Our visit was on a weekday in early June and we had the place to ourselves. Besides we Violetts, there was Cousin Alfred, his wife Emma and two young men that he brought along to entertain Ella and me. They were the Robertson brothers from Sussex — William who was twenty-one, and his younger brother Andrew who was eighteen and very bookish. William Robertson was a sturdy young man with craggy features and the most engaging smile. He had large hands that looked as though they were used to physical labor, and his face was burnt a ruddy brown. His clothes were completely fashionable, but were worn with a careless manner and lacked the perfection of fit of the dandy. He looked older than his reported twenty-one. I will tell you more about him later.

It was a lovely sunny day, and we spread our picnic cloth on the bank of the castle lake under the shade of the substantial remnants of a once massive oak tree that looked so old it must have been a sapling when the castle was built. Across the lake, the weathered brown walls of the little castle, glowing golden in the sunlight, were reflected in the blue water.

After our lunch of "pasties," fruit and wine, William, who incidentally was a keen naturalist and amateur gardener, asked me to walk with him around the lake to see what interesting shrubs and trees grew there. He was supposed to be Ella's beau, but, engrossed in a conversation with

Cousin Alfred and Ma on her favorite subject, the rules of etiquette and court precedence, she made no complaint. I thought Ma looked at me a little sharply, but perhaps it was my imagination.

We strolled across the bridge that led past the ruined barbican to the castle gatehouse, formed by two massive rectangular towers, with a deep arched overhanging parapet between them. High in the gloomy arch we could see a few remaining points of the bottom of the portcullis. It was a grim place to stand in, and it felt good to pass out into the warm sunshine of the courtyard. Here was that peculiar quiet found within massive walls, noticeable even when there is no particular noise outside for contrast. All those background noises that we block out of our conscious hearing really disappear in such places, and we hear the true, almost absolute silence.

That was how it was for William and me. All we could hear were a few bees in a wild berry bush and a slight soughing of wind over the old, crenellated tower tops. It was a very private moment that made us both suddenly aware and a bit embarrassed about being so alone together, so we did not tarry long but "popped" back through the gateway into the world of the present and safe reality.

On the south side of the lake we came upon the ruins of a formal garden that fell away in terraced steps along the slope of the hillside. Much further to the south, across a checkered landscape with the river Rother running through, we saw the soft green hills around the little town of Nortiam — their near sides in delicate shadow, their tops crowned in new green foliage.

William was ecstatic over the old garden and was on his hands and knees in an instant with no thought for the soiling of his clothes. I don't know what rare or seemingly extinct species he found, but his cries of delight soon brought the rest of our party to investigate the commotion. William commandeered a serving spoon and most of the napkins to dig up and wrap samples of his discoveries for later replanting in his family's greenhouse.

On the way back in the carriage William was in a very gay, boisterous mood, and made continuous remarks about what good luck I had brought him and how I must come and see the plants and flowers after they had been re-potted and that I must go on many more explorations with him. Ella began to look very irritated and tried to change the subject, but William had the bit in his teeth and there was no stopping him.

That night at the inn, after a very frosty evening with Ella, Ma came to me as I was brushing my hair before bed and asked me to apologize to Ella, who had complained that "I had stolen her beau." I got rather angry because all this was ruining one of the loveliest days of my life and said, rather cruelly, that if Ella had been a little less interested in manners and more attentive to William, he wouldn't have asked me to walk with him, so it was all her fault and I would rather die than apologize. So saying, I threw myself onto the bed and burst into tears.

At that moment Ella came in (we were sharing the room) and she burst into tears as well. Ma looked at us both for one horrified moment, then she too burst into tears. That startled Ella and me so badly that we stopped and both went to comfort her, whereupon the picture of us struck me so funny that I started laughing, then Ma started too, and Ella, after one confused moment, joined in and we made such a noise that the woman in the next room pounded on the wall.

Ella and I made up, but there was an element of truth in her accusation. I had stolen William's heart, but I did not know it then and neither did he. We wouldn't find out until it was too late to do anything about it.

On a trip to the Isle of Wight in late June of that year to see the yacht races at Cowes, we stopped off to see the famous castle of Arundel, still the ancestral home of the Dukes of Norfolk. Here was a mighty castle combining strength and such beauty as to put one in mind of legendary Camelot. With the massive keep on its great conical mound of earth in the center the outer crenellated walls enclosed a large oblong area of five or six acres, punctuated at strategic points with efficient-looking fighting towers. Arundel is a corruption of the French word for swallow, and somehow this monster of a castle would hardly find such a delicate name appropriate except that some unknown genius of a builder magically gave such an ethereal quality to it that it seems to float above you like some castle in an illustration for a child's book.

Cowes in July of 1870 was simply magnificent. The harbor was filled with the most glorious yachts. Their white sails flitting across the blue waters, polished brass fittings and varnished spars gleaming in the sun, was one of the loveliest sights I have ever seen.

We had the great good fortune to be invited for a day's sailing on the yacht "Ladybird," a lovely 135 foot schooner owned by Lord Hastings, a young friend of Cousin Alfred's. He was very handsome, vastly wealthy, and had the reputation of losing huge sums of money on horse racing. He was said to have lost 100,000 pounds when a horse named "Hermit" won the Derby over his horse "Kangaroo" in a snowstorm in 1867 — a loss that many people said was poetic justice, for two years earlier Hastings had eloped with the girl to whom Hermit's owner was engaged. He carried her off from the back door of Swan & Edgars on Piccadilly while her fiancé waited for her at the Regent Street entrance.

Ma did not go sailing with us on the pretext that Minnie was too young and she must stay with her, but actually she was terrified of sailboats, even one so large as the Ladybird. Our party of six (Ella, me, William, Andrew and Cousins Emma and Alfred) took a carriage down to the jetty from which we were rowed out to the Ladybird in a beautifully appointed little boat called a "gig" by four burly, uniformed seamen. We three ladies sat in the stern and our male companions in the bow with the rowers in between. Once on board we had a delicious four-course luncheon at a table in the stern, set as if in a dining room ashore with fine linen and silverware engraved with Lord Hastings' coat of arms.

During the meal our host entertained us with a marvelous story about a fellow member of the Royal Yacht Squadron that he felt would amuse us because it concerned a battle of the American "Civil War," as they call it in England. His friend, Mr. John Lancaster, was cruising his yacht "Deerhound" off Cherbourg when he sailed into the middle of a fight between the "Kearsarge" and the "Alabama." The Confederate ship was sunk and Mr. Lancaster rescued her commanding officer and a number of her crew and took them back to Cowes. When he presented the Alabama's captain at the Royal Yacht Squadron clubhouse, one of the members turned to his companion and remarked, "Good Lord! Do you think we should offer him a glass of sherry?"

Soon after luncheon the Ladybird's monstrous sails were laboriously raised by a line of twenty seamen, and we were underway. It was glorious to feel the huge boat heel to the wind and charge through the waves, sending great gouts of spray flying away from the bow. There were other boats about like ours, and they made a splendid sight as they pounded along with all their many sails filled and straining at the masts. At one point in the afternoon, another schooner came in so close to us that the sailors were able to swing out on ropes from our boat, catch the rigging of the other boat and hold there for a moment before they swung back again. It was so exciting to watch them, especially when you thought what would happen if they lost their grip on the rope and fell. We all arrived back at the hotel as glowing and crimson as the sunset in the western sky.

We visited the Bronze Age mounds and, of course, Carisbrooke Castle, where King Charles I was imprisoned before they took him to London and beheaded him at Whitehall. I always liked that story about him wearing two vests to the execution because it was so cold that day and he didn't want people to think he was shivering out of fear.

From the Isle of Wight we crossed over to Lymington, where carriages were waiting to take us to our hotel in Bournemouth. Later on a day trip down to Swanage we stopped to see the battered remains of Corfe Castle where, in the absence of her husband, Lady Howe and only twelve retainers held the castle against all the might that Cromwell could throw against it for four long years. Finally it was battered into submission by cannon fire and then blown up with explosives. One towering wall remains and in its face are the holes that the stair-risers were set into. Up and up they go, finally reaching a black empty doorway near the very top of the wall. What room was that? Who looked down from its tiny window at Cromwell's forces ringing the castle walls so far below? Oh how I hated Cromwell for destroying such a lovely creation.

William Robertson and his brother were with us a lot that summer, and William and I became fast friends. Though he was Ella's "beau," he seemed to delight in talking to me about politics, a subject that he was passionately interested in and one that bored Ella, who felt such topics were unladylike and was glad to have me absorb his dissections of prime ministers and criticisms of foreign policies. I was all too happy to do so. I basked in this attention from an adult, and the sound of his delightfully deep voice thrilled me. I read the papers avidly to be prepared for him and found my initially pretended interest becoming real.

We discussed the possible effects of the newly opened Suez Canal, Bismarck's machinations, Disraeli and Gladstone, and the abdication of Queen Isabella of Spain. There was news of a Heinrich Schliemann, who claimed to be excavating the ruins of Troy. This subject fascinated both of us, it was so romantic. Fifty year old Schliemann had selected his eighteen year old bride from a field of contestants in a small Greek village the year before chasing down a legend of Greek mythology. William would laugh at me and scorn Schliemann as a "lecherous old man," but he admitted a certain admiration for him.

I could go on and on about that sixteenth summer of my life. It was the happiest of times, and the war between the states faded and receded away to nothing.

Chapter 9

We returned to London in the fall of 1870 to find everyone talking about the great French defeats at Sedan and Metz, the inglorious surrender of the Emperor Napoleon III, the new Republican government in Paris, and the siege of that city by the Prussians. We had originally planned to go to France in the spring of 1871, but as time passed and the siege of Paris continued through Christmas and into the new year, it became evident that we would have to change our plans, so we reorganized our schedule and arranged to go to Naples in April instead.

This proved to be an excellent choice. We had a splendid three months in Italy before crossing over into France. Compared to the South, there was no evidence that France had been involved in a war until we arrived in the outskirts of Paris about three weeks later. Here we saw much the same sights we had seen in Alabama and Louisiana at the end of the war — broken buildings, rubble-strewn streets, trees with branchless trunks, and people listlessly picking among the ruins of their neighborhoods.

Paris itself was in a terrible state, and we stayed only long enough to arrange our transportation back to safe, peaceful England. When our steamer came up to the dock in Portsmouth and we saw Cousin Alfred and Emma waiting for us, we all got a little misty eyed — it was so good to see them.

That winter we rented a little town house on a small side street off Hyde Park. Ma engaged a voice teacher for Minnie who was then fourteen, exotically beautiful, and with a very promising voice, as several knowledgeable people said. If Minnie hadn't always been so self effacing about her many virtues and talents and so concerned about everyone else's welfare, it would have been very easy to be extremely jealous of her. As it was we were all just proud to be her family.

Someone once said that everyone loved your grandmother Minnie so much because she was like Mary in the nursery rhyme that goes:

Why does the lamb love Mary so?
Because Mary loves the lamb, you know.

It was so true! Where did she come from, that little sister of mine? She wasn't like Ma, Papa or any other older member of the family that I ever saw. In fact I never met anyone, male or female, who approached her when it came to being nice without being condescending. She could be so wise at one moment and so full of childish whimsey the next. She could be positively vulgar in telling a joke, and then as righteous as the Pope. No wonder later in her life she was so good with the prisoners at Moysening State Prison. She could talk to anyone on their level without condescension or disadvantage. It was a wonderful gift.

Being settled into a community in London was great fun. In no time we knew all the essential people: the greengrocer, the milk delivery man, the local "bobby" on the patrol — all the people so important to really belonging in a community. To really belong you must get to know them, to know that the bobby's brother was terribly injured in a mining accident and is still recovering and that the headwaiter at your local restaurant grew the largest roses in his garden club.

We lived in the little house off Marble Arch for a full three years, returning to it time and again after long and short absences spent traveling around England, Scotland and Wales. In late August of 1874, we were back in London preparing to return at last to America. That was when I made the most terrible mistake of my life.

William, William Robertson that is, had been paying court to Ella off and on ever since that first trip to Bodiam Castle. This of course had of necessity in those days involved us all, and I saw almost as much of William as Ella did. He and I had become very close in an older brother, younger sister way.

Oh, I just don't know how to put it! Even after all these years it just seems so awkward. Well, in the bluntest terms, one day William came to call and, finding me alone, took the opportunity to tell me something in private. He told me in an awkward, fumbling way that he had come to realize that it was me, not Ella, who he loved and wanted for his wife.

We were sitting in the little parlor on the first floor. I could hear the sounds of people and horses in the street, but in the room was a great silence waiting to be broken. I was too stunned to speak. Not only stunned by William's announcement, but by the realization that it provoked of the true nature of my feelings for him. He was not just Ella's about-to-be fiancé that I adored as a little sister, he was a man, and I had become a woman, and I loved and wanted to marry him. But what about Ella? She had assumed that some day, in his own time, William would ask her to marry him and that she would accept. How many times had she rehearsed the scene in my presence? What could I say to William?

We sat there how long I have no idea — I with my hands clasped over my knees on the settee and William on the adjoining chair, his hand on the arm of the settee, his eyes on my downturned face waiting for me to speak.

Finally I looked up and putting my hand on top of his said, "William, I have great affection for you, but I can't marry you. It would be too unfair to Ella and I can't hurt her." I was about to continue when, at that most inopportune moment, the front door opened and Ma, Ella and Minnie burst into the room, packages in hand, completely unaware of what they had interrupted. There was nothing to do but rise and greet them as though nothing had happened. Oh, what I would have given for just a few more moments of privacy. What years of unhappiness might have been avoided.

We all went to the theatre that night and it was absolute agony to sit so near in the box and be unable to speak. Every time our eyes met, I saw such a torment in his expression. I ached to comfort him, to hear more of what he felt about me, to have him convince me that it would be no betrayal of Ella to accept him. Two days went by before we had the chance to talk privately. We were unexpectedly alone in the parlor for a few moments, but there was no real privacy because Ma and Ella were in the house and might come in at any moment. We were both extremely nervous and our conversation did not go well. He told me that he loved me deeply and asked me if I would reconsider. I wanted to say yes but ended up saying no, telling him that he would get over me and I him, and that it could only end in unhappiness for us to cause so much unhappiness to Ella.

He said that because he would have to break off with Ella we would no longer have the chance to see each other and did I think that if he waited for six months or so and then made a fresh start with me it would be all right. I said no, it was better that the break be complete. He asked if he could kiss me once to say goodbye. I said yes, and he held me and kissed me so tenderly that I almost changed my mind. Instead, I went with him to the front door, watched him pick up his hat, gloves and silver-headed walking stick, clasp my hand one last time and walk out, closing the door softly behind him.

I stood there facing the door, as still as a statue and feeling just as cold and empty. He was gone. I had done the right thing, I told myself — I had done the only thing possible under the circumstances.

These were the thoughts that raced through my mind, repeating themselves over and over as if the repetition would convince me of their truth. Oh, how I wished there was someone that I could confide in! But there was no one.

We were due to leave for America on the twelfth of September, and I alternately dreaded and yearned for our departure. William did not make a formal break with Ella, apparently deciding to just drift apart or perhaps hoping for further opportunity to win me over. I don't know, but it meant that we were all together for a number of uncomfortable occasions before we left, and the hypocrisies that we uttered to one another were terribly hard to endure.

When the ship sailed I remained on deck. England's disappearance over the horizon seemed to me to symbolize the finality of my decision, and I thought sadly that now it was time to go home and pick up the traces of our real life. Things must surely be back to normal now.

How wrong I was! Life in New Orleans was even worse than when we had left almost four years earlier. The situation had polarized between the Southern whites and the carpetbag rule of the tyrannical Kellog régime. Dedicated to white supremacy, the White League, of which Atwood was a member, had procured arms and formed themselves into what they called a "citizen soldiery" to oppose the forces of the Metropolitan Police under the carpetbag government of so-called "Mayor" Kellog. On September 14, 1874, while we were at sea on our way home, there was a bloody battle between the two, the police were routed, and the White League took over the city hall and held it for four days before surrendering to Federal troops sent in by President Grant. As a result the Kellog government was ousted, and the political fight that ended in the destruction of carpetbag rule began.

The fighting was over by the time we arrived home, but civil disturbances continued to erupt from time to time and life in New Orleans was still very uncertain. In the summer of 1875 we went north to the lovely resort hotel at White Sulphur Springs, West Virginia. Europe and William seemed far away in distance and time. We enjoyed ourselves, and Ella had a brief flirtation with a young lawyer from Ohio who was there with his mother.

The winter of 1875–76 in New Orleans was extremely cold, and we found ourselves shut in a lot. We were nervous and irritable and we seemed to be continually bickering. By the end of February Ma could stand it no longer. Atwood had taken to spending nights at his club, and young Ned was very confused by our behavior. Ella was continually bemoaning the lack of eligible men in New Orleans, and Ma felt the only solution for everyone was to get away again, so March saw us in New York on our way to England and France once more. What mixed feelings I had about that trip.

This time we went directly to France. After a miserably cold and rough crossing, we arrived at Le Havre on a raw, windy day in late March. Again we stopped at Rouen and visited with our relatives there before pushing on to Paris. What a change we found on our arrival! All the war damage had been repaired, and the city was decked out to receive visitors in the grandest, gayest fashion that only Paris can achieve.

We did all the tourist things, met many members of the city's society, and went to many splendid affairs. It was all very dazzling and everyone had a good time except me. Despite the fact that I had held out no hope to William and could expect nothing from him, I was desperate to get to England. I felt sure that he would hear of our arrival and somehow we would meet. I had no idea what it would lead to, but I was yearning to see his crooked smile more than I thought it was possible to want anything in the world!

We spent the summer months at Deauville and Biarritz and finally crossed the channel and reinstalled ourselves in our little house off Hyde

Park in late September. I was so exhilarated I felt I had champagne in my veins instead of blood. At three in the afternoon I begged off from the unpacking and persuaded Ma to let me take Minnie for a walk in the park.

It was a glorious day with just enough cool breeze to take the edge off the heat of the sun and rustle the thin carpet of green and gold leaves on the path. Arm in arm we strolled beneath those magnificent beeches with their smooth silver trunks twisting up into the blue afternoon sky. Over towards Kensington Road, a group of men were exercising some high-spirited horses that pranced and pirouetted, sending up clouds of dust that looked like golden smoke in the slanting sunlight.

I have to admit that much as I was enjoying the scenery, I was paying more than a little attention to any man that even slightly resembled William, and once my heart pounded as we came up to a gentleman sitting on a bench reading, but he looked up as we passed, and it was a stranger.

Everywhere I went that first week I looked hopefully for William's distinctive figure. Several times more I was sure I saw him, but was disappointed in each event. Then Ella came in for tea one afternoon and I could tell from the flash of anger in her eyes and the stiff way that she held her shoulders that something had disturbed her considerably. She flung herself down on the couch where Ma was pouring tea and thrust a news clipping under her nose.

"Just look at that," she huffed. "You might have thought he would have had the decency to at least write me. I mean we were as good as engaged!"

With a growing sense of dread I put down my cup and walked behind the couch where they were sitting to look at the clipping over their shoulders, and it was lucky that I did because the shock it gave me almost made me faint. As it was I was able to regain some composure before they turned to me for my opinion.

The clipping was an announcement of the "marriage of William Ashcroft Robertson to Miss Cynthia Blakely, daughter of . . . at . . . Church on September 2, 1876 . . . the happy couple . . . in Italy . . ." The salient words sprang at me from the clipping. The world seemed to stop. I couldn't move or breathe. Something heavy in my throat seemed to drop into my chest.

I don't suppose it all took more than a few seconds really, and then Ma and Ella's faces were in focus, looking up at me waiting for my reaction. Ella's expression showed anger and self pity; Ma's disappointment and the merest glimmer, I thought, of understanding that I might be more involved than I had let on to anyone.

I stuttered out exclamations of indignation and condolence for Ella and retreated to the window to compose myself with my face averted. Minnie, who had sat unspeaking through it all, came up behind me and took my hand in hers and squeezed it hard. She never said a word or even looked in my direction, but just stood there beside me looking, as I was, blindly out the window. I don't think she had any idea what was going on, just knew I was suffering and wanted to help.

Later, in my room, I smothered my face in my pillow and cried until there were no tears left in my body. How could he do this? And so soon! He couldn't have loved me very much after all. If that was the kind of person he was, I was better off without him! Anger, remorse, self pity, despair, anger again and the whole cycle would start over until I thought I would go out of my mind. What was I to do? Here Ella thought *she* was the injured party. I couldn't tell her the truth, but I couldn't hide my feelings for very long. I had to get away. I had to talk to someone or go mad!

I had met a number of nice young women my age during our previous stay in London, but had found none to become intimate with, certainly not to a degree to talk about this. Then Emma Martin occurred to me. She was older, but she had always seemed so understanding and so friendly. Would she at least respect my confidence?

I sent a note around to her the next day asking for an interview, and she replied that she would be happy to see me that afternoon. Waiting in her parlor for her to come down, I thought that I would either faint or bolt. I did neither, and after some trivial chit-chat and some gentle prodding from Mrs. Martin, who saw before her a girl in the deepest distress, I took the plunge.

Once started I couldn't control myself and I drowned the poor lady with my woes and tears. After I got my crying, sobbing, hiccuping and gulping over with, she simply said, "My dear, how would you like to spend a week in the country with me? I have a friend, a young widow, who lives near Sevenoaks in Sussex who has asked me to come to her whenever I can get away. I'll send her a letter telling her we are coming; we'll go down on Thursday, and I'll keep you busy until then so you won't be around your family too much."

And that is exactly what happened. Without fuss or bother she carried me off to the country where we spent a quiet week with her friend, walking and talking during the day and sometimes late into the night in front of the fire after her friend, Mrs. Wilkinson, had gone to bed. Gradually I got some "perspective" as she called it, and I didn't think I had to die anymore.

It helped a lot that she knew William's family quite well and also the family of the girl he had married, who turned out to be someone he had been a close friend of since childhood and who had always had "her cap set" for him. I began to see how he could have gone to her with his troubles and ended up marrying her as he did and, as the French say, "to understand is to forgive." I might begin to forgive, but I still felt awfully out in the cold and somehow I wanted William to know how miserable I was, but at the same time I would die before I would admit it to him.

Cousin Emma, as she asked me to call her, handled me with perfection, and our relationship grew from that time to become one of the most precious of my life. She is still alive today and I exchange letters with her regularly.

I was able to return to London in full control of myself and was relieved to find that William and his marriage had become a forbidden topic in our household. We spent the fall pleasantly enough, but somehow William's marriage had discouraged Ella to such a degree that she seemed to abandon her ambitions in the matrimonial field. Ma, too, was depressed and moody, spoke wistfully about returning to America, and finally decided to cut our trip short. We had to wait until March before we could secure a passage that Ma felt safe about and even then she was very nervous, but we had a good crossing and arrived home vowing never to go back.

Atwood Violett
33 West 51st Street
New York City

October 28, 1925

Dear Mally,

I seem to spend more time lately writing you letters than writing the story, but I need to put in a personal note here before I go on with it. It's just for you.

After the blow of William's marriage I did suffer terribly for a while. During the following years I had several interested gentlemen friends, but the relationships never blossomed into proposals of marriage. I'm afraid there was something about me that inhibited them. When it finally came to me that I would never marry and have the family that I had always hoped for, I was very depressed. Still, in time I got over it, and when I stopped feeling sorry for myself I slowly built a new life — quite a good one I think.

As they say, I am a "spinster," and that has become a very harsh and misunderstood word in these modern times. I was not born to be a spinster, quite the contrary as you know, but I want you to understand that despite its obvious drawbacks spinsterhood has certain great advantages. In the first place, a spinster is not some withered tree whose sap has ceased to flow; in fact it can flow all the stronger for not being soaked up in the practicalities of marriage.

A married Emily Dickinson would have been too busy with her husband and children to have spent those long hours at her window contemplating the changing seasons and finding time to write about them.

Take Oscar Wilde, for whose work I have always had the greatest admiration. Could any full member of society so accurately describe its weaknesses and strengths as he did in stories like "The Importance of Being Earnest" or "The Picture of Dorian Gray"? I think not. The spinsters, the bachelors and the others whose lives are different from the norm can, if they have the art, serve society well by holding up a mirror for it to see its own backside.

Ever since I was a little girl, my whole life was pointed at marriage; I never suspected that it would be otherwise. I was poised, ready to step into a beautiful future when suddenly that future disappeared. I would have been a good wife and a loving, concerned mother and when I realized that this was not to be, for some time I felt that life was meaningless. I ached to marry, but would not marry without love, and my feelings for William kept getting in the way of establishing new relationships. I burned with jealousy of married friends with husbands and children. I felt left out, cheated, rejected, and sometimes even ugly when, in all modesty, I knew I was a rather pretty woman with a good head on her shoulders, was intelligent without being forward and a good conversationalist. Life seemed very unfair.

Then, in 1879, I met a Mr. David Humphreys at a party in Philadelphia. What he told me then and in many conversations since changed my whole perspective of the world and of myself. He has done considerable study of the Hindu and Buddhist religions and seeks to blend their principles with those of the western world. At our first meeting he described his recent travels in India and said that he found considerable similarity between their religious views and those of Christ. He was quick to add that he didn't mean Christianity as propounded by the established church, because he felt that was a perversion of what Christ had actually said, made to suit the church's own self interest — to control people — whereas Christ's purpose was to set them free. (David's views were very radical for that era, and he was careful to keep them quite private. He mentioned this at the time and said that he was quite surprised to find himself making an exception in my case.)

David said that, in the deeper sense, Christ and Hinduism agree that man is truly the son of God, not by virgin birth as in the myth of

Jesus, but by God recreating himself in every sentient living being, so that He experiences all the joys and sorrows of the world. "I am the son of God, and you are too." That, in David's opinion, was Christ's message, His Gospel.

"Certainly," David said, "it would be no good news to mankind for Jesus to announce that He was the *only* son of God!"

I recall that in a recent conversation he alluded to this point by quoting G.K. Chesterton's poem:

> But now a great thing in the street
> Seems every human nod
> Where move in strange democracy
> The million masks of God.

As opposed to the traditional Christian, monarchial view of God as the supreme ruler of the world, Jesus as His Prince, Mary as the Queen Mother, and the Catholic Church as the high court and army of the true faith, David, like the Hindus, conceives of God as the supreme Actor, playing His own role as God and also the roles of everything else in the whole universe. It is what David calls a "dramatic" concept of God.

David has explained to me what he calls "the balance of life," where good and evil, pain and pleasure, life and death — all the opposites of the world — go together and define each other, the one being unable to exist without the other. For instance, there can be no front without a back, no outside without an inside, no light without darkness to shine through. You wouldn't know you were hot unless you knew cold, or vice versa.

Of course David makes no claim to be the first Westerner to hold these views, citing examples from the works of poets, authors and philosophers from Shakespeare to Emerson, but only to some originality in their application.

From this beginning I began to see the world differently. To quote Blake:

> To see the world in a grain of sand,
> And Heaven in a flower,
> Hold infinity in the palm of your hand
> And Eternity in an hour.

Trees grow and branch out into the sky, dividing into smaller and smaller limbs, and under the earth the roots are a hidden mirror image of the tree above. In exactly the reverse process, rivers grow from many tiny branch streams flowing down into the main trunk of the river. The arteries, veins and capillaries of human bodies are exactly similar in design to the forms of trees and rivers. All living things, in fact, can be reduced in principle to networks of tubes for ingestion, digestion, distribution, and egestion. Everywhere you look in the world, you see nature using a few simple mechanical and architectural concepts over and over in a myriad of combinations. And all of nature's creations are members of one family because of their common structure, from the simple rock to the dazzling complications of a human being.

David is the only person I know who has pointed out how inconsistent it is for Man to talk about conquering nature when Man is part of nature.

I learned about Hai Ku poems that use so few words and imply so much: "In the dense fog, what is being shouted between hill and boat — "

He told me about the Japanese "moods" with strange names like Ugen, Aware and Urushu — each expressing a feeling that cannot be defined, only described by example, like the feeling of mystery on seeing a pathway that winds up and over a mountain. Where does it go? Why are closed doors so mysterious and intriguing?

He told me the allegory of the man who struggles up a difficult hillside to get through a door in a wall and, upon finally passing through, turns and finds that both the door and the wall have disappeared — to illustrate that man struggles to reach what he thinks is a better place and finds that he is already there.

Another "mood" that I like is illustrated by thinking of a man who stands in a river fishing, and is aware not only of his pleasure in the sport, but in the thought that to someone observing the scene, he is adding an important accent to its beauty. No wonder Chinese landscape paintings almost always have a small fisherman in a corner.

Still another admires the tree that grows out of the barren rock. Or is the rock barren? Wasn't the whole world once one huge "barren" rock? The rock is operating in a different time dimension, hundreds of thousands of times larger than our fourscore and ten. Eventually the rock will flower into plants, animals and finally into people. Because this happens too slowly for us to observe, we can't appreciate the phenomenon, but do not be fooled — we are descended not only from apes, but ultimately from rocks. "Do not despise rocks," David would say.

He showed me the tricks that time and space can play on the senses. For instance, the constellation called the Big Dipper is only real, that is it only looks like a dipper, from one place — the planet Earth.

Time and directions like North and South have no reality, they are mere conventions for arranging a meeting. He liked to say that you couldn't tie up a package with a line of latitude or longitude.

G.K. Chesterton put it so humorously:

"It is one thing to describe an interview with a gorgon or a griffin, a creature who doesn't exist.

"It is another thing to discover that the rhinoceros does exist and then take pleasure that it looks as though he doesn't."

So easy to confuse reality and convention.

It's also easy to feel totally excluded from life because you are not doing the conventional thing. For a woman, of course, that means getting married and having children. Before I met David I felt lost and alone. He changed all that, and gave me a feeling of belonging in a world that I had never known before. Life isn't simply what people say it is.

Looking over the last few pages and realizing that I have put forth some pretty radical views, I hasten to say, lest you think your old Aunt quite mad, that though I subscribed to all of David's views, and they did wonders for me, I almost never spoke of them to others. I knew how shocked most people then would be, and I had no desire to be thought a religious radical. Now in these modern times when "anything goes," I feel a little more comfortable in exposing my opinions, and, even though your Groton upbringing probably makes it difficult for you to accept these ideas now, later in life you may appreciate them. In any case they're part of me, and I'd like you to know about them.

I have gotten more than a little carried away here, but what I was originally trying to say is that although the war completely destroyed any future I might have had in the South — I never became a great Belle of New Orleans, or wife to a rich planter to stand with my daughter on the gallery of my mansion and watch the steamboats on the Mississippi — and I missed out on my only real chance at marriage with William — nevertheless, I have been able to lead a full and enjoyable life. I have a philosophy that works for me, and have had many wonderful, deep, incomparably rewarding relationships with many people: like David Humphreys, Cousin Emma, your dear, sweet mother, and you Mally — especially with you.

Up until this point I have been telling you about the Violetts and about myself especially. I apologize for dwelling so much on my own experiences, but this delving into the past has uncovered some emotions and memories that I thought were long buried. In a way it has been very good for me to relive them. As Cousin Emma would put it, I can put them into perspective now. I thank you for bearing with me.

Now I'm going to tell you about your mother and your Whelen grandparents. After I had put William Robertson out of my life, Minnie's marriage to Charlie Whelen made them the center of the lives of all the Violett sisters; everything revolved around Minnie, Charlie and their children, and our own ambitions faded into the background.

Back to the book!

Aunt Lily

Chapter 10

It was so good to get back to the States in the spring of 1877. Everything seemed so wonderfully "American." I know that sounds funny, but it's true. There is a wonderful simplicity and freshness about this country that you must go abroad to appreciate.

We arrived in New York on a bright sunny morning in late March and after clearing customs, settled into a suite at the Plaza (the old Plaza now — the brand new Plaza then). Since we had not planned to return to New Orleans until the fall, we stayed a while in New York, then made our way by stages down to Washington to spend some time with Uncle Robert Gray Violett in Alexandria.

In early June we stayed for two weeks at the "Bryn Mawr Hotel" in Bryn Mawr, Pennsylvania, before going to spend the first of many summer visits to Atlantic City. We were drawn to Bryn Mawr because of its reputation as a first-class resort despite its unusual location and origin.

In the late '60's the railroad was expanding its network of tracks in this area and decided to create an exclusively residential neighborhood in the vicinity of the little hamlet of Bryn Mawr. The houses erected on Montgomery Avenue, the main thoroughfare, had to cost the imposing sum of no less than $8,000 — those on the other avenues, $5,000. Setbacks and other restrictions were imposed through the conditions of sale, and the net result has been a magnificent grouping of fine houses devoid of neighborhood stores, shops or livery stables. These were all allocated space in a convenient central location. The only "commercial" buildings in the residential area are (or were) the three hotels: the Bryn Mawr, the Lancaster Inn, and on the very edge of the area, the old White Hall Hotel.

The Bryn Mawr was the best of these. Being so close to Philadelphia, it permitted an easy commute for businessmen who could not afford a long vacation in Maine or Canada. It was so pleasant a place that wives were content to stay with their husbands, who were equally pleased to be near the source of the family revenue and enjoy the company of their families. Consequently, it was full all summer.

Besides the summer guests there were "regulars" who lived at the hotel year round — older people to whom the hotel had become a combination home and club. I remember one in particular, a loveable little dried-up old bachelor who had piled up a large fortune — some said by never incurring any expense that he could avoid. He used to ride to and from the railroad station in the hotel bus until he found out that it was being charged to his room bill at a nickel per trip, whereupon he persuaded his friend and fellow hotel guest, Mr. E.Y. Townsend, to give him free transport in his carriage. He liked to tell everyone how he had put one over on the hotel.

Your grandmother was nineteen that summer and radiant in her new womanhood. She was about five foot three in height with a fine figure, nothing like the flappers of today. I was the tallest sister at five six and slightly more slender than Minnie. Ella was somewhere in the middle on both counts. Ella and I had brown hair like Ma's, but Minnie's hair was a very dark brown, almost black, with deep lustrous depths in its natural curls.

Minnie's skin had a wonderful honey shade that complemented her deep brown eyes. With those eyes and her full-lipped mouth, she could be more expressive than any person I ever met; it gave her a tremendous advantage as a singer and an actress. (I hasten to add that she only acted in amateur performances. Professional actors were still regarded as déclassé then, but amateur theatrical associations like the Acting Club in Philadelphia that your grandmother belonged to for many years were all the rage in society.)

As I have related, your grandmother Minnie had a fine natural voice and started taking lessons during our winter in Toronto. Since that time Ma had made sure that she got regular coaching, so that by the time I am now speaking of she had a lovely, well trained voice and a good repertoire. She was often asked to perform, and one night, while we were at the Bryn Mawr, she was asked to sing in a musicale sponsored by a group of the "regular" ladies at the hotel.

As she was singing I noticed a very tall, blond-haired man come quietly into the salon and find a seat at the side of the room near the little platform-stage. It was your grandfather Charlie Whelen, of course, and he couldn't keep his eyes off your grandmother, even when she was seated between her performances. When she finished a song, his applause persisted quite a lot longer than anyone else's, and after the recital was over he was the first at her side to congratulate her.

They were married on October 16, 1878, at our home in New Orleans. The house on Prytania Street never looked better. The Reconstruction period in the South was finally over, and the city seemed to have regained all of its ante bellum gaiety. The whole Whelen family came down from Philadelphia for the wedding, and they made such a contrast with the New Orleans people. Charlie and his three brothers — Henry, Alfred, and Kingston — were all over six feet tall, blond-haired, blue-eyed and fair skinned, and dressed in simple dark suits, while most of the New Orleans crowd were short and dark, wearing brightly colored vests and neckcloths.

The church on the square was packed. Minnie was breathtakingly lovely in her white wedding dress with her veil flowing down over her bustle and an exquisite S-shaped rope of flowers from hip to hem across the front. Walking behind her as one of the bridesmaids, I could see Charlie's sudden look of wonder melt into one of absolute adoration as Minnie walked down the aisle toward him. (Just for the record, Atwood gave his sister in marriage, and Henry Whelen was his brother's best man; Ella and I were bridesmaids and Ned was the head usher.)

The wedding was at eleven, and we were back at Prytania Street by noon for the reception, which lasted until late into the afternoon. Charles and Minnie had a suite that night at the St. Charles Hotel and sailed for New York the next day. We all went down to the levee to see them off, and there was much good-natured frivolity, especially between the Whelen brothers, and much weeping by the females present. Then suddenly there were Minnie and Charlie standing at the rail of the ship; and there we were waving from the shore as the ship turned out into the Mississippi, and they were gone!

The Whelen clan left the next day by train for Philadelphia, leaving us to ourselves after almost a week of festivities. The sudden quiet and unusual inactivity put me into an unexpected state of depression. I was happy for your grandmother, but I was very unhappy for myself. Strangely, Ella didn't seem to be bothered at all. At least she didn't show it, but then she was usually very good about keeping things to herself.

I thought a lot about William and wondered what was happening in his life. I had heard absolutely nothing about him since England, except for seeing the mention of his name in a gardening periodical as having designed a formal garden for some lady in Kent. How my heart leapt within me at the sight of it. Did he even remember me still?

We spent a quiet winter in New Orleans. It was pleasant to re-acquaint ourselves with its now restored peaceful personality. Ma had a long illness, though, that prevented us from entertaining too frequently, but she recovered completely by springtime, thank goodness.

Atwood was proving himself to be his father's son, going from one business success to another. Ned, now twenty-two, had thrown himself into the business of enjoying himself, and his drinking and gambling were a real worry to us. Still, there was little Ma could do; he had come into his inheritance from Papa that year and although the sum was far from large, he was, for the moment, independent.

Your grandmother Minnie enlivened our winter by her letters from abroad, and then from Philadelphia after their return. As a wedding present, Charlie's father had bought them a house on Walnut Street, just off fashionable Rittenhouse Square, where they invited us all to pay a visit in the spring. Needless to say we accepted with alacrity.

Minnie's new home brought out all my feelings for an architectural job well done. I must describe it to you as I saw it that first time in April of 1879.

It was typical for its time and for the area, an upper class neighborhood of the city. It was five stories high, about twenty-two feet wide and sixty feet deep, and the front was flat and even with its neighbors on either side. Entering the front door you found a wide, steep staircase on the left, and a reception room on the right. Beyond that was the front hall, and beyond that an arched doorway led to a coat closet, storage rooms and a door leading to the rear of the building. .

As with many town houses of that era, the kitchen, with servants' quarters above it, was in a separate two-story building in the rear, joined to the main building by narrow corridors on the first and second floors. This arrangement kept the cooking smells and most of the servants' rooms out of the main house. There was a dumbwaiter that connected the first-floor kitchen to the basement where food supplies were kept, and to the second floor, where the prepared food was taken through to the dining room located just opposite the living room which was at the front of the house.

The dining room was made bright and cheerful by a large window area with a central fixed pane of glass, opening double-hung windows on either side and a high fanlight above. A long mahogany table was set lengthwise from the hall doorway to this window parallel to a fireplace on the right-hand wall and to a large sideboard on the left. Gaslights on either side of the mantelpiece and on the opposite wall supplemented the candles on the table in the evening.

The living room took up the whole width of the building. It was large and very formal, with molded plaster panels on the walls on either side of the fireplace and similar decorations on the ceiling, which on this floor was sixteen feet high. Heavy red velvet curtains with an ornate gold fleur-de-lis design were draped in rich arcs on either side of the two tall windows overlooking Walnut Street and complemented a similar color that was in the basic theme of the oriental rug on the floor.

Over the mantel was a large portrait of Mignonette wearing a red velvet dress with matching cape and holding in her hand a sheet of music. On the wall opposite the fireplace were two huge gas-lit "candles" in sconces, and between them was a large round mirror with a deeply carved gilded wood frame.

The doorways from both the dining room and the living room opening onto the central hallway were eight feet wide and about ten feet tall. A continuous parquet floor ran from the living room through the hall and into the dining room, uniting all three rooms into a spacious whole when doors were open.

The third and fourth floors were devoted to bedrooms. On the third floor, Charles and Mignonette's overlooked Walnut Street, and there was a guest room on the same floor in the rear. The fourth floor contained two more bedrooms for guests or for children when they came along. The fifth floor was for servants' rooms and for storage. Here the ceiling height was reduced to a bare seven feet and even on the sunniest days the small rooms seemed dark and mysterious.

Apart from these servant areas, the whole house was elegantly furnished with deep carpeting on the stairs, oriental rugs in many rooms, heavy, polished mahogany furniture and gleaming brass gaslighting fixtures casting a warm light over all.

It was a delightful house, combining warmth, security, and graciousness — so different in style from anything in New Orleans. For me, Ella and Ma, it became a new focal point in our lives. We continued to spend a great deal of the year traveling, but we were with Minnie as often as possible.

Minnie was so completely genuine in her desire to have us with her, and Charlie, being tied to Philadelphia by his business, seemed so glad for us to be her companions that we never felt as though we were outlasting our welcome. We became one big family; it was almost good enough to make up for not being married ourselves.

Our attachment to Minnie and her life in Philadelphia was even further increased when in the spring of 1880 Minnie announced she was with child. We enjoyed her condition almost as much as she did. She had a very easy time of it, and at 8:45 P.M. on the 9th of December she gave birth to your mother, a perfectly formed little girl — well, not so little — Dr. Smith said she was one of the largest babies he had ever delivered. But she was unusually beautiful. She had a full head of fine silky brown hair at birth and she never lost it. It was about two inches long and lay flat against her head, giving her an almost adult look. She had an adorable little rosebud mouth that puckered up when she was fretful and, most strangely to us Violetts, she had blue eyes. Obviously the Whelen blood was very powerful to overcome that of the dark-complected Violetts, Oldhams and Martins.

She was called Violett Whelen, in accordance with our family tradition.

She and her cousin Elsie Whelen were Christened together by Dr. Watson at the Holy Trinity Episcopal Church on Rittenhouse Square on the 26th of April, 1881. Minnie was in a state because Violett was making her "talk" noises the whole time, and when it was over she was so relieved she burst into tears.

Minnie wrote about it in her journal:

> . . . She was Christened the 26th of April. Mrs. Leavitt came over from New York to be Godmother number one. Mrs. Frailey was No. 2. Mrs. L. gave her a very handsome fork and spoon and Mrs. F. a perfect pin . . . She and little Elsie Whelen were Christened together. Violett puckered her little rosebud mouth up for a cry when Dr. Watson put a very big handful of water on her head, but the minute she heard his deep voice she changed her expression into a happy one. She talked the whole time. I was so relieved when it was all over that I cried and startled everyone. I felt that Baby had received God's seal; that Charlie and I were sharing partnership with God in the care of our dear little Violett. She was God's child now as well as ours . . . Oh! I do hope and pray that I may bring her up to be a good Christian woman and to live the Christian life . . .

Dear Mally, your mother Violett Whelen was such a lovely person and as a little girl she said so many cute things that I feel that I must quote from some more of Minnie's letters and journal to give you some idea what she was like. I hope they will interest you. To me they are so typical of her personality, but then I knew her so well and you not at all. Your mother was such a mixture of her parents. She looked so like her father, yet she had Minnie's personality to a degree that was uncanny.

In a letter written from Atlantic City on June 20th, 1881, Minnie wrote:

> Today Violett (six months old) said "Papa" distinctly for Ella and once for the nurse and she tried very hard to say bye-bye after me. I am so afraid she is too smart. I only nurse her at about eleven and then again at daylight. She is so little trouble and such a world of pleasure. I give her the bottle once a day and she has only had one little cold since she has been out. I gave her camamilla, a homeopathic dose.
>
> I do enjoy having Ma and the girls rave over the baby. Violett is so exquisitely formed. In the first place her little

head is round all over, her little cheeks fat and rosy and her eyes the most luminous, expressive and intelligent ones I ever saw in a baby's head. Everyone raves over her eyes. The whites are very blue. Her mouth is a perfect cupid's bow. Then her hands and feet, though large, are exquisitely shaped and her limbs taper so beautifully. Her little back is as straight as can be and not a bone visible and her chest is so full and round. In enumerating Baby's points I feel like the mother in a little poem who says:

> I count her beauties, as the nun
> Counteth her beads o'er, one by one
> So many ways my fond heart finds her fair
> It makes each breath a grateful little prayer.

For indeed whenever I look at Violett I wonder what have I ever done that God should have given me anything so perfect? Charlie and I thought our life very happy and complete before she came and we can scarcely realize what we ever did without her before . . . I have often said it is a wonder that I don't end up in spontaneous combustion from my great pride in Violett.

Atlantic City, June 30th, 1881 — Baby had on her first short dress today. It made me feel sad to take off her long dresses. I realized how time was flying and how each day makes her less and less Mama's baby . . . Lily and Sadie Thompson make her laugh more than anyone else.

Atlantic City, July 3, 1881 — Violett cut her seventh tooth. This morning I had her by the window and it was too funny seeing her try to catch a fly. She followed it up and down with her hand until she finally caught it.

There are many more letters and entries in Minnie's journal, and perhaps someday you will want to read them, but in the meantime these excerpts will give you some idea what your mother and grandparents were like.

Because I used to keep your great grandmother Sarah Whelen company a lot, I picked up a good deal of family history. I won't bore you with a long recitation, but here is just a brief summary.

Your grandfather Charlie Whelen's family were of Irish descent. The original name was "Faelan," or "Little Wolf," which was anglicized into Whelen. James Stevenson Whelen, the first known to use the name in that spelling, came to the United States in the 1690's and in 1694 married a Sarah Elizabeth Denis in New York. Their son Denis Whelen was the first Whelen to settle in Pennsylvania.

Your grandfather, Charles Smith Whelen, was the son of Townsend Whelen and Sarah Yates McElwee. He graduated from the University of Pennsylvania and in addition to business had a strong interest in music. That, of course, was how he met your grandmother.

He was not a very aggressive person, but he had a set to his jaw that showed determination and strength. I saw these qualities often during the troubled times that came later. He was a great fan of college football even though he wasn't athletic himself, and he always had tickets to the Saturday game. We had some wonderful times watching grown men butting each other around the playing field like a bunch of billy goats.

He wasn't much of a talker in a large group, but when you got him alone, he could expound with the best of them. Minnie was the witty one at parties and he was content to sit back quietly and enjoy her pleasantries.

After they were married, Charlie joined his brother Henry (the "handsomest one," as he was referred to when the brothers were compared) in his father's business, as was the custom of dutiful sons in that era. The company offices were at 309 Walnut Street in Philadelphia, and Charles and Minnie lived at 2017 on the same street, so it was a straight carriage ride downtown in the morning and back at night. The coachman that took him was reputed to sleep the whole way, and Charlie said that he felt that the horse could just as easily do the whole job on his own.

His two younger brothers, Alfred and Kingston Goddard Whelen, were perhaps not quite as handsome as Henry but still handsomer than almost anyone else I ever knew. Finally there was the youngest sibling, a sister, named Sarah, after her mother, who was as tall and blonde as a Viking princess.

Alfred, known as Fred, became a doctor, married Sarah Wurts

Smith and had two sons, Townsend and Thomas Duncan — the latter of course, being your guardian when you were growing up. Alfred was a great horseman, riding with the local hunt clubs at every opportunity.

Henry, although undeniably a pleasure to behold, was frankly a little too perfect for my taste. I preferred Alfred's broader, more relaxed way of living. Henry and his wife Laura had two daughters, Laura and Elsie. Elsie Whelen was almost exactly your mother's age and, as I mentioned before, was her best friend.

It was a tightly knit little community centered around park-like Rittenhouse Square, and your mother had many nearby friends and young cousins in the neighborhood — such as Bertha Lippincott, who lived at 2101 Walnut Street, and Marie Lemoine whose family lived at 2113 Delancey Street, only a few streets away.

Summertimes we saw little of Philadelphia except when, of necessity, we passed through it on our way to somewhere else. In New Orleans, people left the city in the summer to get away from Yellow Fever, but in fact there was a summer exodus from all large American cities in those days. They were unbearably hot, dirty, and reeked of horse dung, urine, and industrial odors that were simply suffocating. Open the windows and the smells were unbearable; shut them and exist in an airless oven. Those were the options.

There was only one solution. Get out of the city if you could afford it. The men were tied to their work, but those who could sent their wives and children to the seaside and country resorts that sprouted everywhere to accommodate this demand.

Charlie and Henry Whelen had summer houses in the countryside just west of Philadelphia from which they could commute to the city. Henry's, called "Clovelly," was in Devon and Charlie and Minnie had a small farm in Morestein in West Chester called "Nestledown." Minnie, your mother, and your Uncle Charlie (and we Violetts when invited) spent the early and late parts of the summers there, and the middle part at summer hotels in resorts on the Atlantic coast.

In September 1881, Minnie wrote in her journal:

Violett has a very great peculiarity. She is afraid of dolls.
Her first doll was a little rubber one which Ma gave her at the
age of three months. She would have nothing to do with it

and would deliberately throw it down. Also a rubber doll sitting in a chair that Mrs. McInerny gave her. She is so afraid of a doll with hair on it that Mother Whelen gave her she nearly goes into fits. I think she was frightened when she was seven months old by a little kitten and she has never liked anything hairy since. Even a little piece of fur or false hair. But the doll has a horrible fascination for her. She wants it yet she shakes with fear when she touches it.

I do wish this 10th tooth would come through. She shivers with the pain. She has not slept well for three months, day or night. Mary McPink, her nurse, is so faithful and patient . . .

Baby also plays the piano and sings. Oh, she is so bright and lovely and such a blessing. She is going to have an affectionate disposition.

Back in Philadelphia in November 1881 Minnie wrote:

She calls her nurse "Mamie." The moment I strike up "Yankee Doodle" she breaks into a broad grin, daintily picks up the end of her dress and moves her whole body. If she could stand she would dance. She calls for Papa's tic-tic and is so devoted to him. Charlie is just the man to have children, for I know he can bring them up well, he is so strong in his character and so loving. He always plays with Baby when he comes in. The little thing cut her twelfth tooth at ten months. I have to get a little tooth brush for her, just think of it!

Exactly three years and one day after Violett was born, on December 10, 1883, Minnie gave birth to a beautiful blue-eyed, blond-haired boy who was named Charlie after his father. He was almost as much loved as your mother and he added just what was needed to make their lives complete.

In July 1884, she wrote:

He is the most perfect little darling, so good and he is growing larger and prettier every day . . . He is not sick I am thankful to say. He does not say anything yet. He is an even better baby than Violett. I mean he sleeps better at night. He is such a laughing baby, he always has a great smile for us all, such an angelic little smile. He has a cute way of bumping heads whenever we say, "Bump heads booful" and when I am kissing him he turns my head around to see my earring. He is a very powerful child, beautifully formed with a beautiful head. His eyes are so lovely now. He had a sore eye for four months and it was finally cured when he was vaccinated, which took so well and was so severe that we think it took all the inflammation out [of his eye].

Then later in the journal:

Violett says so many pieces now. One is:

Mother, mother may I go swimming?
Yes, my loving daughter
Hang your clothes on a hickory loom
And jump right in the water.

But the funniest thing she does is with an Irish accent:

Come to my arms Norah darling
Bid your friends in old Ireland goodbye
And it's happy we'll be in the land of the free
And me name it is Barney McCoy.

It is too funny to hear her correct her nurse. I heard her one day say, "Lizzie, you must not say 'raiburns,' you must say 'ribbons'."

Every morning she comes to our door and says:

Here's a proud young lady
A noble young lady
And a little sleeping beauty!

All with a rising inflection on the last word.

This summer at her evening prayers she has been reciting "Jesus tender shepherd" only for the second verse she says, "All this day Thy hand hast led me — And I thank THY for

Thy care — Thou hast clothed me warm and fed me —
Listen to MY evening prayer."

One afternoon she saw a rainbow and of course wanted to
know all about it. I asked her who lived in the heavens and
she said, "Mrs. God, Mother."

The other night Ida Grant asked her how much she loved
her. She measured on her fingers and said, "so much." Charlie said, "Well, dear, how much do you love Papa?" She was
sitting beside him and in the most impulsive way she threw
her arms around his neck and said so earnestly, "With all my
heart!" Charlie was very touched . . . Bless her heart, I have
great hopes for a lovely ripe womanhood for my little girl.
God has endowed her with a beautiful nature and I feel a
great responsibility to keep it so and by His help I will try.

In August of 1884, Minnie wrote me the following:

Violett was quite naughty the other day and when her
father asked what made her so and why she did not try to be
good always she said, "I do try, Papa, but I cannot keep the
goodness inside me." I do pray against spoiling her and I do
earnestly try to be strict, but she is a child to be governed by
love. She is overflowing with life and animal spirits. Up to all
kinds of mischief but never bad.

Mally, your mother composed her first written "story" in 1888 and
gave it to me. I still have it. It was about a dog named "Worry" that the
Whelens owned. Worry was a Basset hound with a particularly mourn-
ful expression. "One day worry was siting in the yard. Suddenle he herd a
noise. Worry jumted in surpis to see a puppy standing busid him. They
got to be frind and lived haply evre avter."

In February of 1889, Minnie was in New York visiting her friends
the Leavitts and acting in an amateur theatrical performance. Your
mother, then nine, wrote her mother:

Dear Mama, You ought to have seen the little indian
yesterday. The Indian was me! Uncle fred came over and said

I had the German Mealies. Please do not worry about me or you will make me very miserable.

I had the best time Saturday. I heard so much about Japan that I drempt that I was in a tea house. Miss Carter looked out the window and saw some fish moving about in the air. At last she saw that they were fastened to poles. She got dressed and went and asked the cause. The man said that long ago there was a king that went out hunting and he got separated from his men. He came to a little brook with a waterfall one foot high and he saw a little fish that wanted to jump over. Mama I have to tell you the rest in another letter. I hope you will be a success in the play. Do not show this letter. Goodbye from Violett.

Folded in with the same letter is a piece of paper with a draft of a "Composition on God":

God is very good to everybody. He gives you everything you want that is good for you. God showed a great deal of love for His people when he sent His Son to die on the cross. A very few people cared about Jesus being crucifiede. As they walked to the spot where He was to be crucifiede He had a crown of thorns on His head and they pushed it down on His head until the blood come. God lives in heaven. Sunday is God's day, it took Him six days to make the world and Sunday was the day he rested. God is very powerful. He does wonderful Miracles. The most most wonderful Miracle that God ever did was to make dead people alive. — Violett.

That last line makes me shiver to read it now, it was so foreboding.

Violett liked to watch her mother dress, especially when it was for one of her operatic or theatrical performances, and Minnie said you could tell she was making mental notes of every little detail. Then she and young Charlie would put on little plays in which she would re-enact adult scenes that she had observed. With the help of their nursemaid, they would build a stage out of steamer trunks next to the hall doorway to Violett's bedroom on the fourth floor and use old blanket covers for curtains.

She and Charlie put chairs in the hallway and used the doorway as a proscenium arch. Then they corralled anyone that they could find for an audience. Violett was very adept at mimicking her elders, and she often had us in tears laughing at her parodies of people we knew. Many a rainy winter afternoon I spent with Minnie and Ma and a servant or two watching your mother's performances.

Minnie encouraged her singing, and by the time Violett was fifteen they were performing duets at musicales. Her purer, thinner voice blending with Minnie's rich contralto made a lovely combination. It delighted me when I was in my room at the Walnut Street house to hear mother and daughter practicing in the parlor below.

There were few sports for women in those days, but I think that if there had been she would have done well, because she was physically well coordinated like all the Whelens. Tennis was becoming a fashionable thing at that time and she and Elsie played often. Of course it was a different game then, especially the clothing. For a woman to move with any speed, it was necessary to grip one's dress and undergarments firmly with the left hand and swish them out in the direction you wanted to go before you moved yourself. To do this and then hit the ball required much skill. I tried to play once and made a spectacle of myself when I tripped and fell on the grass.

When Violett was fifteen and on vacation at the White Hotel in Atlantic City, she and Cousin Elsie hired two of the new "safety" bicycles and rode out into the countryside one afternoon. It was a great adventure, two young Victorian girls out alone in the world. We heard the details repeated and embellished by girlish imagination for weeks afterwards.

That same year of 1895, Minnie and Charlie felt that more formal arrangements for your mother's schooling should be made to take the place of her rather casual and sporadic attendance to whatever schools or tutors were available in Philadelphia and on her travels.

Formal education for children of the well-to-do at that time was the cause for much argument between parents. Fathers generally held with the patriotic sentiment that American public schools were the best in the world, and therefore it was somehow disloyal to send one's child elsewhere. Mothers, who were frightened of added exposure to diseases such as diphtheria and scarlet fever, not to mention "undesirable acquaintances," and the greater chance of knowledge of "certain things" too soon, advocated private schooling. Usually, the mothers won out with the argument that there were better sports programs at the private schools and that the fresh country air would promote strength and health.

But all that was about boys' education. When it came to girls, there was no question. They had governesses, went to private day schools or had tutors, and then, perhaps, boarding school at about fourteen or fifteen. I remember reading Judge Robert Grant's "Art of Living" where he said that a woman should study moderately hard until she is eighteen, then look as pretty as she can and devote herself until she is married to having what is called on this side of the Atlantic a good time. In other words, four years of whirl and then a husband or no husband and a conservative "afternoon tea drinking spinsterhood."

I would argue with him about the restriction of spinsters to "tea drinking," but he does sum up the usual sequence of events in the life of a young girl from an upper class family.

So in the fall of 1895, fifteen year old Violett was sent to Dana Hall in Massachusetts. I visited her there several times and fell in love with the institution. Dana Hall in 1895 was a small school of about one hundred pupils, with only three buildings located on a few acres of land on Grove Street just outside the little town of Wellesley, Massachusetts. It was an offshoot of Wellesley College, which had been started in 1875 by Henry Durant, an educator who passionately believed in the intellectual emancipation of women. The world of 1875 was, as he put it, "either indifferent to higher education for women, dubious about their need for it or downright hostile to it" and he intended to do something about that. He felt it "a sham notion that women should be trained only in 'accomplishments' " and thought they should have access to the same courses of study as males.

However, when Wellesley College opened in September 1875, only thirty of the 314 students enrolled passed the placement tests. Making a "truce with necessity," the trustees created a college preparatory department for the remaining 284. This department was dropped in 1880 because there was no longer room for it at the now full college, and Durant had arranged to start a preparatory school called Dana Hall, which opened in September 1881. He was fortunate to find two wonderful spinster sisters, Julia and Sarah Eastman, as co-principals for Dana Hall, who were to carry his desires for the school far beyond his original expectations.

I still have a copy of their brochure in which they say, "It will be the aim of the School to combine thorough Scholarship with a symmetrical womanly culture . . . [meaning manners and deportment]. Pupils completing the Preparatory Course will be received at Wellesley College without further examination. The School will offer advantages for special study to pupils not contemplating a College Course . . . "

Your mother loved the school. It was made to order for her even if it was rather bucolic and isolated compared to fashionable Philadelphia and the other cosmopolitan areas of the world that she had lived in. She was always anything but a snob and soon made friends with other girls. Besides three of her closest friends from Philadelphia — Elsie Whelen, Bertha Lippincott and Marie Lemoine — were there, so she had little cause to be homesick. It was such fun to visit with them and have tea in Violett and Elsie's room with its Harvard and Yale banners on the wall above beds piled deep with many pillows. Violett, whose bed was in the corner next to the window, had about a dozen on hers. The walls were covered with photographs, scores of them, including, in a crimson frame, the eleven members of the Harvard football team of 1894 in their uniforms.

Well, as I told you before and as the above amply illustrates, your Whelen grandparents, your mother, and your uncle Charlie became the most important people in my life after our return from Europe in 1877 and remained so until the tragedies starting in 1903, but in the meantime the whole relationship with William Robertson boiled up again in a most dramatic fashion.

Chapter 11

Seven whole years went by before I had news of William again, years during which I never forgot him, but learned to live with the dull, almost physical ache of missing him. Oh, I would forget him for a time, but then something would prick my memory and his presence would come flooding into my mind with an intensity that was hard to bear.

Then in February of 1883, while we were in New Orleans, I received a long letter from him. It read as follows:

Dear Lily,

I know it will be a shock to hear from me after all these years, but I am finally giving in to an overwhelming need to write. I have missed you so much and I feel so badly that when you left things between us were so unresolved. I can't go on any longer without talking to you, even if it's only a one-sided conversation in this one letter.

First I want to apologize for the way I acted during the last week of your stay in London. I was a pompous, egotistical ass and I cringe when I recall my behavior. It was so damnably dense of me not to realize the impossible position you were in regarding your sister, but I didn't, and so I couldn't understand why you had turned me down so abruptly.

It was rather awkward for me to continue with Ella after that, but if I formally broke off with her I would not have been able to see you at all before you sailed. I was so desperately hoping that you would reconsider.

Of course it didn't work that way. We had that one too brief talk alone and even then I was unable to tell you what was in my heart. I was so nervous and felt so hurried that it came out all wrong, and afterwards I was completely frustrated at having missed my chance again.

Then suddenly you were gone and it was so final. Never have I felt so irrevocably blocked off, so baffled as to what to do. You have no idea what a state I was in — angry with myself, angry with you, and feeling almost physically sick with the thought that I would probably never see you again. I knew a loneliness such as I had never known before and which, despite periods of happiness, has persisted all these years.

All over now, of course, but it is very important to me to tell you that I regard you as the finest, most desirable woman in every way that I have ever known. I only became fully aware of you as a woman during the last year of our association although, in fact, you had achieved that status much earlier. It was hard to make the transition from my idea of you as the precocious little girl I met at Bodiam Castle. I didn't realize that my comradely affection for you had grown into the truest love that I have ever known. Since you left I have thought of you so very often, remembering and reliving the many times when we were together and thinking what might have been . . .

Ah well, so much for idle dreams.

Let me tell you as briefly as I can what has happened to me since we parted company.

After you sailed I turned for advice and consolation to Mr. Edward Blakely, the father of Cynthia, the girl I then married so precipitously. Cynthia had been an old childhood chum. We grew up in the same town and became friends through our mutual love of gardening. I went home with her one day when I was sixteen and met her parents.

I was immediately struck by how different they were from my parents and their friends. Mine were very social, always on the go, entertaining or being entertained, and totally uninterested in the things that their sixteen-year-old son thought were so important. By then I had begun my fascination with politics and religion and I was continually trying to draw my parents into discussions on such things as child labour laws, the miners' question, what we should do as a nation about the massacre of Bulgarians by the Turks, and whether Disraeli or Gladstone was the better prime minister, etc. (the sort of things you and I used to talk about so much).

Mr. Blakely, on the other hand, not only had a keen interest in these subjects, but was the most incredible source of information. There seemed to be almost nothing he didn't know a lot about. Furthermore, he was always willing to put down whatever he was doing and chat with me.

Cynthia's mother was a rather subservient person, the daughter of an Anglican minister who ran his family rather like his congregation. She transferred this attitude to Mr. Blakely and allowed him to dominate her in a way that diminished their relationship for both of them, for there was little interchange of ideas between them.

However, aside from that one flaw, they were a happy and devoted couple, and Mrs. Blakely was the kindest and most considerate woman to all who came beneath her roof. Her only other fault was her inability to keep the house in order and, since they had no servants, it was always in a state of dust and disarray. To me, though, this gave their home a warmth and coziness that I found an appealing contrast to the cold perfection of my own home.

They and their three children (Cynthia has an older sister and brother) lived a very quiet life and were not in the least "social." They had a few good friends that they saw from time to time, but they did not entertain on a regular basis.

He was "in business," but only moderately successful. I got the feeling his employer resented his superior mind and the strong positions he took and so promoted inferior but more malleable people over him. To me he was the most amazing person I had ever met, and I spent as much time in his company as I could.

Another endearing quality was his fondness for working around his property, which had been a small farm before he bought it. With his own hands, he mended fences, relaid stone walls, put new shingles on the barn, or repointed the old fieldstone chimney of the main house — a strong contrast to my father who felt manual labour of any kind demeaned a gentleman.

I started to help Mr. Blakely with these tasks because it gave me a chance to talk with him, and found in the process that I too loved such labours. There is a wonderful feeling about doing something with your hands that you can look at afterward with pride. Of course this and the gardening interest threw me together with Cynthia a great deal, and I found her such a good audience that when I wasn't listening to her father

I was lecturing to her. We became good friends, but no more, and I continued to drop in on the Blakelys over the years when I had the chance.

So, as I said, when you turned me down I was terribly despondent and turned to Mr. Blakely for counsel. He was very helpful and Cynthia was so comfortable to be with that I spent a lot of time with them until finally, one day, quite unaccountably, I found I had asked Cynthia to marry me and she had said yes.

Soon I began to have some doubts about what I was doing, and I honestly think that I might have called it all off if my parents hadn't raised such a row about it. Their objection was that the Blakelys weren't really their class of people. They were dead set against the marriage, but you know how I am when I get my back up, and of course I found "undeniable" arguments for it and absolutely refused to consider listening to reason, theirs or my own.

And so, with my parents in grudging attendance, we were married, and for a time I put aside all other thoughts and settled into the novel routine of married life.

We lived very simply. Cynthia's family had no money and I, like Mr. Blakely, was only moderately successful at business. I went to work for a local bank, where in time, I have become a department head. Children came along as they will, two girls and a son in that order. They are lovely children and I adore them. They make up a lot for what is missing in the rest of my life and I spend a great deal of time with them.

Cynthia and I soon acquired a small circle of friends, sons and daughters of my parents' friends, couples all much richer than ourselves, all cut from the same dreary cloth and as interchangeable as bowling balls. Nice people but dreadfully predictable and with the same lack of interest in the world that I found so hard to bear with my parents.

Occasionally I would meet an interesting couple on my own and ask Cynthia to invite them over. Inevitably, she would reply, "But we don't know them!" and I would say, "Well, we never will if we don't see them, will we? Please drop them a note." Somehow she never got around to it.

As the novelty of marriage wore off I began to see what a terrible mistake I had made. I realized I was not in love with Cynthia; I didn't even find her particularly interesting. It was her father whom I had admired and become fond of, and marrying Cynthia had been a way to become part of his family.

I feel badly about Cynthia. She is as good a mother to the children as you could want and is completely blameless in this whole situation. I feel like a cheat for having allowed her to marry me under the circumstances, but there's nothing for it now but to go on. Anything else would be too cruel to her and the children.

Thank God for my hobbies, gardening especially. I find great peace in that, but so often when I stop for a rest and a pipe in the late afternoon, you will come to my mind and a great longing and loneliness comes suddenly into my heart. I will recall our day at Bodiam Castle, for instance, when we were alone together to share those magical moments within the walls and later the thrill of finding that ancient garden. You know, I still have the descendants of those cuttings I took, still thriving in their new beds. They are specially precious to me because you were with me when I took them up.

So here I am, settled into a small house, an old gatekeeper's cottage to be precise, with a respected wife and three lovely children, an uninteresting but adequate job, my hobbies, a few cherished friends, and a large number of dull acquaintances — in sum the perfect picture of a settled citizen.

How deceptive that is. I feel so different from these would-be English Country Gentlemen, and to pretend to be one of them and share their mouldy views of life is the most distasteful hypocrisy. I know that I have no real complaint, that I should try to adapt, but I simply can't do it. I am different and I yearn to proclaim my true identity to at least a few special people who can understand. Perhaps that is one of the reasons I am writing to you, Lily.

Well, that's about it, Lily. I hope that you will forgive me and that the knowledge of my love and admiration will have some value to you.

I will never know for certain, because I absolutely insist that you not write me. If you wrote that you did not forgive me I couldn't bear it. If you wrote that you did and still had some affection for me it might encourage me to actions that would be less than just to those here who depend on me.

In my heart I feel that I am safe in believing I shall be forgiven, and I shall be content with that. God bless and keep you, Lily. May you always be happy. I wish only the best for you. As some unknown poet put it:

> May good fortune be ever attending
> To my Lady where e'er she may be.
> Fill her life with joys never ending
> Are the thoughts I am thinking of Thee.

Sincerely and affectionately,
William

That is the letter William wrote me and I cannot tell you how moved I was by it. So, after all, he remembered and cared for me still. For me, too, it was impossible not to think "what might have been" thoughts. If Ella hadn't regarded him so much her property, if he and I had recognized the true nature of our feelings for each other sooner, if we had not left England so soon, if William had not rebounded into such an unfortunate marriage . . . Yet nothing could ever happen between us now; that was clear. He would not leave his wife and children to marry me, and yet he loved me still and God help me, I loved him.

I was desperately sad and yet so proud to be so loved. I was glad to receive that bittersweet letter. William was right, it was of great value to me!

It was lucky that I was alone in the house at the time; it gave me a chance to sort things out before Ella and Ma returned several days later. I read and reread William's letter; in the garden under the shade of the crèpe myrtles, in the evening in Papa's study and in my bed by candle-light, when I would fold it carefully back into its envelope to put under my pillow.

The day Ella and Ma returned I read it over one last time and then put it safely away in the bottom compartment of my little traveling lap desk. I had no need to read it again, but every time I passed by I looked at the dark wood box and thought of William's letter glowing like a warm coal inside it.

That was in 1883. Your mother, little Violett, was three years old and "full of beans" as they say now. Ella, Ma and I were back in Philadelphia in April and spent most of the spring and summer with Minnie, who was pregnant again and, as I told you before, your uncle Charlie Whelen was born exactly three years and one day after your mother on December 10, 1884.

We spent a happy Christmas that year in Philadelphia and returned to New Orleans in February. Ma's joints were painful and she had to get home for the warmth or I think we would have spent the whole winter.

Then in May of 1884, Ma, in one of her typical spur of the moment decisions, announced that we were going back to Europe, and by June we were once more on a steamer crossing the Atlantic.

Chapter 12

I came out of a little shop on Bond Street, and there he was —
walking toward me swinging his walking stick and looking in the store
windows as he passed. I couldn't believe it was him. I was frozen in
place, unable to move, to think, or anything. My heart was going like a
trip-hammer and there was a buzzing in my ears. He stopped to examine
something in a window about thirty feet away and I just continued to
stare at him. He was slightly bent over, looking in the shop window and
then, without straightening up, his head turned slowly in my direction
and our eyes met. His mouth, under his new brown mustache, slowly
widened into a broad smile as his recognition grew. I could see his mouth
form the word "Lily," and then he was striding toward me, arms
outstretched, tears welling up in his eyes.

For long moments we stood together in the doorway, he holding
both my small hands in his large ones, wordlessly smiling at each other.
At last he said "Lily" again, and I said "William," but that was as much
as our choked voices could manage. He placed my hand on his forearm,
still holding it in his, and we walked without speaking down the busy
street. People scurried by us in all directions, shop doors opened and
closed, carriages and cabs clip-clopped by, but it all seemed very distant
and muffled, as though there was a little envelope of silence around us.

Coming into a small park, we found a bench and sat. Now we were
more composed and could begin to talk. Slowly at first and then more
easily until it was as if the past eight years had never intervened. There
was no awkwardness; all the important affirmations that needed to be
made had been communicated without words in those first few minutes
when we came together.

We had met about half after one in the afternoon, and we sat talking on that bench until three, when the bells in a nearby church sounded the hour and woke us from our enchantment. Ravenous, we found a tearoom and spent the rest of the afternoon in it eating and talking. William had become so distinguished looking with his mustache and sideburns, but his smile and the twinkle in his eye were as boyish as ever. It was such a delight to be together.

There were so many questions to ask and so many answers to listen to, and then I simply had to leave or I would never be able to explain my long absence to Ma and Ella. We arranged to meet again the next afternoon at the park, and then I think I floated out of the tearoom and all the way to the hotel without my feet once touching the ground.

We continued to meet over a period of about two weeks. I made great pretense at shopping to cover my absences, declining, of course, any offers of assistance, and returned with just enough purchases to lend credence to my excuse. My emotions during those two weeks ran the gamut from delirious happiness when I was with William to an aching loneliness when we were apart. Sometimes when I awoke during the night I would experience sickening feelings of guilt about being so involved with a married man. I would vow to be strong and break it off when next we met, a promise that I was unable to bring myself to honor once I was again in his presence.

Then it was time for us to leave on the next stage of our tour. I met William the day before we left and we said our goodbyes — not for forever, but just until we returned in the fall, so it was not a very sad parting. We would meet again in three months' time.

During all these conversations there had been no talk of love, no talk of the future, and little talk of William's wife and children. We existed only in the present — only in our own little world. Our unspoken rationale was that since our relationship was innocent and would hurt no one, we were justified in stretching the rules of propriety if our occasional meetings would give us strength to carry on in our separate lives. We rationalized that each meeting would be carefully wrapped up when it was over and put away for review and re-enjoyment in the future. How little we knew about human nature.

So the summer did not pass too slowly for me, although at times when I found myself in some particularly enchanting situation I yearned for William to be there to share it with me. Never before had I realized the truth of that saying that beauty can only be truly appreciated when seen reflected in the eyes of your beloved. And beloved was what William had become. Slowly I began to realize that I couldn't pretend to myself that we were just very good friends, that I was very fond of him, that he felt a similar controlled affection for me. I was in love with a married man and he with me. We should break it off — but not quite yet.

When we met again in London in the fall, I knew immediately by the ardor of his greeting that William had made a similar analysis of his feelings. We both knew that occasional brief meetings would only whet our appetites for more of each other's company than such occasions could possibly provide.

Several weeks later, as the date of our departure to the States drew near, I decided to apply once more to Cousin Emma Martin for her wise counsel. With her I had the blessing of total frankness that I had with no one else. We met for lunch and afterwards walked in Hyde Park, where the lovely old oaks and beeches were sending gentle showers of autumn leaves floating down through the bright afternoon sun. We sat on a bench and I told her everything. She said little or nothing during my long recital, but there was a "tristesse" in her expression just behind her sympathetic smile.

"What am I to do?" I concluded. She turned away from me, her profile stern in thought, her gloved hands resting one atop the other on the handle of her parasol, her short, square figure rigidly erect. Presently she relaxed and replied. "It's dreadfully sad," she said, "but you must give him up. If you don't, nothing can come of it but grief for everyone." She went on, deeply sympathetic and never uttering one word of criticism, but after her initial judgement the rest of her words washed over me almost unheard, as if I had retreated into the back of a cave and she stood outside. I knew she was right, but I couldn't accept a future with no William in it anywhere, anytime, ever.

Her voice stopped, and after a moment I came out of my cave. Then she added, "See him one last time before you sail. I tell you what — there's a house party next weekend in Sussex. Very nice people and not too far from William's place. I'm going and I'll wangle invitations for both of you. Since he and his wife are living such separate lives, I am sure he can manage it without any fuss. Have a nice time with him and then settle things up before you part."

And that is exactly what happened. Fortunately Ma and Ella had engagements in town and had no concern about my going off with Cousin Emma, especially as they thought I might meet some marriageable young man. How far they were from the truth. There must be theatrical blood in the Violett family, I was able to conceal my emotions so effectively.

Our hosts, Roger and Catherine Olney, owned a large Elizabethan manor house in Sussex southeast of East Grinstead near the hamlet of West Hoathley. On Thursday afternoon the train took Cousin Emma and me as far as East Grinstead, where we were met by a carriage sent to bring us and another party to the manor. Turner's Hill Road took us to Vowels Lane and the entrance to the thousand-acre estate. The land sloped gently down past Duckyll's Wood, through Warren's Wood, past the home farm, then down a long manicured drive with tall trees and green lawns on either side and then there it was — another house to add to my collection.

Green ivy, reddened in many places by the fall season, covered much of the walls, lending them such depth and color that they glowed like fire. Rippling in the gentle afternoon breeze the ivy gave an air of animation to the building that was quite unusual in my experience.

In design the house was a slight modification of the usually perfectly symmetrical "E" of most Elizabethan manors built to honor the Virgin Queen; the central projection of the "E" was closer to the base and contained the covered entranceway. Five massive chimney breasts were spaced across a slate roofline broken by dormers of varying sizes. Three more chimney breasts ran from the front to the back of the left side of the manor, where a large ell had been added in recent times.

Surrounded by enormous elms, oaks and beeches, the house's ivy-covered walls so blended with the arboreal background that the house looked to be part of the wild forest itself. To the west the land fell away with a splendid panoramic view of distant hills and valleys across a wide field of oats that sloped steeply down to a small stream that fed a little unseen lake to the south.

Inside, paneling of oak or birch and figured plaster ceilings were the unvarying rule in all the rooms. There were large fireplaces everywhere, sometimes two to a room if it was a large one, and I thought to myself, Well, at least I won't have to worry about the usual problem of keeping warm! Indeed, I was to discover that these fireplaces were most remarkably efficient, having been built to the owner's special design — one involving the use of heavy cast iron plates on the base and back to absorb and retain the heat. Even in the morning, when nothing remained of the logs burned the night before but the ashes, these plates continued to radiate a considerable amount of heat.

Cousin Emma and I were shown to our rooms by the butler. The Olneys were not visible, but we were told that we would see them at tea time. Our rooms were in the northwest corner of the house, looking out over the field to West Hoathley. To the north was a large garden area that had obviously received little professional attention for many years. How that will displease William, I thought and then I saw him crouched over something at the far end of the terrace. Making hasty explanation to Cousin Emma, I flew down the stairs and crept stealthily up behind him. "I believe you are the gentleman who stole the plants from Bodiam Castle, sir," I said. "I am Constable Violett and I have been on your trail for many years. Now I have caught you red-handed! Consider yourself under arrest!"

He turned, laughing, and rose to take my proffered hands in his, and so began our last weekend together.

The company assembled for tea in the great hall at four. It was a mixed group in all senses of the word. There was a stiff, self-conscious young American couple from New York City, an elderly pair of brothers who were neighboring landholders and so rotund they reminded me of Tweedledum and Tweedledee, young Lord Peter Weldon and his lovely raven-haired bride Pamela, three young gentlemen from London whose names I cannot recollect, and, of course, our host and hostess and their daughter Rhona, a spinster about my age.

Roger and Catherine Olney were in their mid fifties, both rather stout and of a florid complexion that told me they spent much time out of doors, a guess later confirmed by their ardent descriptions of the local hunt. Most of the other guests were down to ride with the hounds, a fact that proved most useful to William and me over the next few days since I didn't ride well, and William, who did, claimed a game knee.

At dinner that night, I learned that the Olneys had met Cousin

Emma and Cousin Alfred when they were both on honeymoon in Venice and had been good friends ever since. I sat on Mr. Olney's left, and he described some of their adventures with the Martins and told me how much he was saddened by Uncle Alfred's untimely death of typhoid three years previously. When he discovered I knew nothing of horses or foxes, he turned his attention elsewhere and I was free to talk to William, providentially seated on my left. How delightful it was to be with him in public like that.

For the next three days we were left on our own while the others rode to the hounds. We walked or went on buggy rides all over the surrounding countryside. The weather was warm and sunny with that special crispness in the air that only fall can produce. We stopped at village pubs for our lunch, enjoying that country delight the "plough-man's special" (a slab of bread with cheese and pickles), washed down with a pint of bitter. Once, when we were not going far, we carried a picnic and a bottle of chilled wine in a small hamper.

William bought a large-scale ordinance map in the village, and we used it to guide us to the "public pathways" that meander so intimately through otherwise totally private property. Like a little child, I pretended we were trespassing in enchanted woods where dragons lived and that each high window in some stately home hid all sorts of romantic secrets. As a woman I walked arm in arm with William, savoring each moment of intimacy, absorbing each sight, sound and smell for the future. I remember thinking of a stanza of Tennyson's "Day Dream," so perfectly in tune with that lovely, bittersweet day that I quoted it to William.

> And on her lover's arm she leant,
> And round her waist she felt it fold,
> And far across the hills they went
> In that new world which is the old.

Then it was Sunday, the last day. After a lovely picnic in a high meadow, we were sitting in the buggy on a little country lane admiring a small stream passing under a rustic footbridge, quite obviously delaying our return to the manor. No mention had been made of the future until then, but now the imminence of our departure made it necessary. After a long silence I started to speak, to say the words that meant, in short, goodbye forever, when William interrupted me. "No, Lily," he said, "it is my place to say it. I know we can't go on and it's my fault for being so weak and selfish to allow us to get this involved. Living without you will be the hardest thing I can imagine, but there is no other way; I've too many obligations to meet, but I'll always keep you in my heart as long as I live."

He put his arms around me, kissed me softly, and held me close for a long, long time. Then he picked up the reins and we drove in silence through the gathering dusk to the manor. He helped me out of the buggy, held me for one brief moment, and let me go. I walked up the stone steps and pausing at the top looked back. He stood where I had left him by the buggy watching me depart. He smiled a sad version of his special smile at me, touched his fingers to his lips, and blew me a kiss in a slow sweet gesture. I returned it and entered the house.

A footman brought me a note before dinner from William saying that he felt it best to leave, so had pleaded urgent business to his hosts and had himself driven to the train station. I was relieved in one sense because I had dreaded being with him for the rest of the evening, and yet I was heartbroken not to see him one last time. It was a long and dreary dinner, and I was so unresponsive to everyone that Cousin Emma finally declared to the company that she thought I was coming down with something and took me off to my bed. As she was straightening my pillows, I said, "William's gone."

"I know," she said. "We'll talk about it in the morning."

Chapter 13

For the second time I was back in America, lonely and broken-hearted, with the broad Atlantic and the even more formidable barrier of society separating me from William. I had no choice but to rebuild my life yet again.

By this time Ella had settled into the "tea drinking spinster's" life predicted by Mr. Grant, but I was too restless for that. We each had a small personal inheritance from Papa, and now I used some of mine to travel on my own. In the spring of 1885 at the age of thirty-one, I packed my things in the smallest number of trunks and cases possible and set out to see something of the new, booming United States of America. Ma and Ella were against the project, but Ned and Atwood, bless their hearts, overcame this opposition. Ned offered to come along, but I wanted to travel alone and being a "spinster of mature years," it was perfectly proper for me to do so. Atwood made banking arrangements for me in appropriate cities along my route of travel and friends of the family wrote letters of introduction to useful people.

For six months, from April to November, I traveled across the country. I went by riverboat, by train and by stagecoach. I stayed in cities from Chicago to Boston to Charleston, South Carolina, and many lovely rural areas in between. I visited old friends and made new ones.

First I went to Louisville and Cincinnati and found that the war-bred ill feelings between us and our relations in those cities had disappeared. It was so nice to be on comfortable terms with them again. There were still politicians who waved the "Bloody Shirt" and would for many years to come, but despite their bombastic oratory, most people were willing to forgive and forget. Although the towns were much enlarged since we romped through the fields on our summer vacations, there were enough of the old landmarks to make me feel nostalgic tugs. It gave me a strange feeling to see some of my cousins' children now the same age as we had been during those ante bellum summer visits.

In May I traveled to New York and saw the newly completed Brooklyn Bridge, the most impressive span I have ever beheld. I was fortunate to be invited to attend the premier performance at the new Metropolitan Opera House, a far grander edifice than its older cousin in New Orleans. For the occasion I was provided with a handsome escort by my hostess, but I'm afraid he found me cold company. It was silly, I know, because he was very nice to me; it was just that it seemed somehow "unfaithful" to William to be nice to him in return.

New York was fascinating. How it had changed in the few years since we were last there. Only two years earlier it had become the first American metropolis to light its streets with electricity. Electric lights seem so garish compared to gas; I still can't get used to them when they shine in my bedroom window at night. You're used to them, of course, but you can't imagine what a shocking difference they made, when they first appeared, to those of us reared in the gaslight era.

I spent two weeks with my old friend David Humphreys and his now large family in Princeton, New Jersey, where he was employed as a teacher at the university. I confided in him about William and he was so sympathetic and understanding. What a wonderful thing it is to have such a friend, a man in tune with the times but also in tune with the larger world, the world beyond "times," the ever evolving but never changing universe. David used that "perspective" that I have mentioned before to my good advantage during those two weeks, and I left Princeton feeling far stronger and more able to face my future.

In July I was in Newport for a month at the incomparable Ocean House, where I got a chance to drive one of the little basket phaetons drawn by a pony that were all the rage then. I found Newport society interesting to observe as a grand spectacle, but rather boring to endure for any length of time. The husbands of the chatelaines of those imposing summer houses rarely appeared and seemed to prefer their business associates in New York to their wives and children in Newport. They sent their excuses in letters with large checks enclosed as though they were renting their absence for yet another week. The wives, on the other hand, felt obliged to empty their just-filled purses as quickly as possible in order to make room for the anticipated new infusion due before the next weekend. To quote Henry James imperfectly, his Newport lady tells her English guest, "It is an American woman's duty to buy something every day, and if she cannot do it herself she must send someone to do it for her!"

What a shallow relationship those people had! How could a woman be satisfied with it — or a man, for that matter. They were supposed to be married, but they spent more time apart than together. Thank God Charlie Whelen was not as smitten with the business fever as these "Barons of Industry." Yet I can see how seductive the game of commerce was then to a man of affairs. There was as much money to be made hunting in the woods of Wall Street as there were buffalo to shoot on the Western plains, and it must have been an extremely exciting and all-consuming occupation. Who could blame a man for succumbing to the temptation of bringing down big trophies in business and rationalizing that he was doing it all for the ultimate benefit of his wife and children? And who could blame the wife for accepting the situation and playing her role as it was presented to her by her husband, one of the all-powerful male impresarios of her world? I understood how this could happen, but it didn't make the participants appealing to me in any way.

Washington — Alexandria, Virginia, to be exact — was my last port of call before returning home. There I found Uncle Robert Violett in good but fragile health at the age of seventy-five. His mind was reasonably lucid, his hearing moderate, his sight for distance quite remarkable and his sense of humor as bright and sunny as ever. Earthy, sometimes a shade indelicate but never vulgar, he was a delight. I got the impression that he sensed that something momentous had occurred in my life. I considered telling him, but despite his humor he was very moralistic so I thought it better left alone.

I ended my "sabbatical" by returning home through Charleston, South Carolina, and Mobile, Alabama, in late September and October. I wanted to see with my own eyes Charleston Harbor and the famous Fort Sumter. The harbor was quite beautiful, but the fort was a terrible disappointment. I had envisaged a massive castle-like structure, and I found a three-storied stone building with a hip roof and chimneys. It looked more like a stodgy hotel than the mighty fortress depicted by the Southern press in 1862. How truth is bent for purposes of propaganda.

Throughout my travels I read enormous quantities of books. There were so many good ones being published then by authors like Flaubert, Anatole France, Henry James, de Maupassant, Stevenson, H. Rider Haggard and last but not least, my favorite — Mark Twain, as sophisticated and elegant in an American way as any foreign writer. There is something especially satisfying about reading when one is traveling alone. A good book is almost as satisfying as a good companion. If I began to think too much of William when I was in bed at night, I would light my candle and be transported into another world.

When I returned to New Orleans in early December of 1885, I had not forgotten William nor changed my feelings for him, but I had filled my mind with many new ideas and personalities with which to divert myself. Having dreaded my return to reality I was surprised to find that I was truly glad to be home with Ma, Ella, Atwood and Ned.

However, if I had not gone away, home would have seemed a jail and one where silence was the rule. I still could not bring myself to confide in Ma or any other family member about my affair with William. Now I had put six months of distance between myself and that weekend in Sussex. I had talked at length about him with David Humphreys, who had given me hope for a new future on my own. If William was not out of my heart, he was at least out of my life, which now lay with my family — especially with Minnie, Charles, little Violett and little Charlie. Oh, how I longed to see them! How I wanted to hold those children close to me, to pour all the love I had in me into their lives, and to be important to them.

I wrote Minnie, and she invited me to come in the spring. I spent a great deal of time that winter buying clothing and toys for the children. To do so made me feel I was already with them and so helped to alleviate my great impatience.

The winter of 1885–86 was a hard one in New Orleans. It was exceedingly cold and stormy throughout the country, and in late February there was a long warm spell in the North that sent great torrents of water down the river. Massive breaks in the levees caused great areas of flooding all through the South bringing sickness and near starvation to many people.

Ma's health had been poor for some time and she was hard to live with. Atwood, Ella and Ned were of little help. Ella had reinstated (or reincarnated) the same clique of female friends she used to rule when she was a little girl. They were not all the originals, but the new additions were so similiar in character to those they replaced it was hard to tell the difference. Ella was continually on the way to or from one of their houses and spent as little time with Ma as possible. In a way, this was a blessing because she was so critical of Ma and me and the servants when she was home that she just made everything much worse. If even one chair was moved from its proper place, she would have a fit.

Ned was twenty-nine then and leading a less than exemplary life. Ma said he could give college courses in hedonism — which was an exaggeration, but not by much. He was a renowned club man in a city that had more clubs than any other city in America. We urged him to marry one of his many lady friends. We felt it would give him purpose and save at least one lonely Southern woman from spinsterhood, but he would have none of it. His club-mates were all the family he wanted, and he worked only enough to keep his income within hailing distance of his debts; his unpaid bills were a constant embarrassment to the family. Time after time, Atwood rescued him from his creditors.

Ned was uncorrectable, though. His attitude of humility and regret for his impositions when reproved made it impossible to remain angry with him for more than five minutes. He was charming and flattering without giving you any feeling of manipulation. He never boasted of himself — only of others. In short, despite his lamentable style of living he was the most loveable man, and he had more friends in the city of New Orleans than you could believe possible.

But he was no use when it came to Ma. She alone seemed impervious to his charm and only dwelt on his neglect of her. She nagged him so about it that it made him stay away even more, thus giving her further proof of his lack of consideration. In reality he loved her very much and understood that he was her "whipping boy" for all her troubles, but it pained him deeply that he could not have her affection.

Atwood, too, had his paramount interests outside the home. Ever since he became his own man in business when Papa died in 1868, he had gone from one business success to another. His association with his father's old partner, Mr. Black, proved to have drawbacks, so in 1871 they dissolved that partnership and Atwood formed a highly profitable one with two contemporaries, William McGehee and John Snowden. That lasted until 1879, when the unfortunate death of Mr. McGehee in a duel forced its dissolution. An older man, Mr. I.E. Glenny, with a considerable business as a cotton broker, asked him to handle the contract work for a new partnership for a fifty percent share of the profits. Since Mr. Glenny would provide abundant capital, Atwood accepted, and they remained partners until Atwood married Olga and moved to New York in 1893.

Atwood was very active in Louisiana politics from the time of Papa's death. In the 1870's he was a member of the "White Camelias," a branch of the "White League" that eventually re-established white supremacy in the state, and later he was a captain and then a lieutenant colonel in the Crescent Regiment of the Louisiana National Guard. Between his business and these activities, he had little time to spare. He came home to sleep, have breakfast with us, and then was gone until late at night. If we were lucky, we might see a bit of him over the weekends.

I could see from all this that if I were not careful, it would be very easy for me to become Ma's permanent companion, bound to her by chains of duty and dependency. I was determined that this should not happen for both our sakes, and it was as much for that reason as my own selfish desires that I went alone to spend the summer with Minnie and her family. I found a useful and soul-satisfying niche for myself in her family, and soon became a permanent part of their lives.

And so the years went by, spent in small part with Ma and Ella in New Orleans, and in large part with Minnie and her family — in Philadelphia during the winter and at hotels or Nestledown in the summer. Year after year, I was with your mother and your uncle Charlie as they grew up. Often Minnie would leave them in my care if she had an engagement out of town. Those were very special occasions for me, when I could have little Violett and Charlie all to myself. Minnie, God bless her, recognized my need for this substitute motherhood and never spoiled it by any pettiness.

From the small round-faced cherub in the long lace christening dress, to the self-possessed five year old with bangs and a level gaze, to the shy, long-legged, long-haired twelve year old, to the final emergence of the young woman endowed with beauty, proportion, grace, intelligence, human understanding and compassion that your mother became, I was there — not just as a witness, but as an integral part of her life, not only for the good times, but the bad as well. I helped her dress for parties and I held her head when she was sick. I said yes she could and no she couldn't.

I don't mean that I took your grandmother's place — hardly that. Minnie was a most conscientious mother, but I filled a role somewhere between mother and older sister, between mother and governess, that was complementary to Minnie's position and I like to think your mother became a better person because of that — having, in a sense, two mothers.

I shouldn't neglect your uncle Charlie. He was an exceptional person too, and held almost as high a place in my heart as his sister. In all honesty, I think that the reason I gave your mother pre-eminence was because I identified with her so. She was to have all the things that the war and subsequent events had prevented me from enjoying — the ordered stable life, the uninterrupted progression from childhood to womanhood to marriage and motherhood. I wanted her to be worthy of them and to appreciate their value — and so she grew to be.

Look at me, I'm doing it again — two lines of Charlie and then six of your mother.

Poor Charlie was born into the era when little boys from well-to-do families were subjected to the indignities that sprang from the cult-like worship of the novel "Little Lord Fauntleroy." From baby dresses they progressed directly to a costume of velvet pants and shirtwaist with a large lace collar and cuffs to match. Admittedly, this outfit was only worn on formal occasions like meals with the grown-ups and visits to relatives, but there was no escape from the ever present shoulder-length hair that the fad also demanded.

Charlie bore it grudgingly. You can see for yourself in the pictures taken at the time his expression of weary submission to these unmanly indignities. I must admit that I was as taken with the fad then as Minnie. It is only now, looking back, that I can see how silly we were.

As he escaped into more self-respectable clothing you could see the signs of his coming development into powerful manhood. From the age of about nine, he was half again as big as other boys his age and well coordinated too. He was fond of sports not only for themselves, but also

145

because he was somewhat on the plump side and had a horror of being "fat all my life," as he put it.

For an older sister and a younger brother, he and Violett got on extraordinarily well together, aside from the little spats that flared up when Charlie would do something mischievous to tease her, or when she would get a little too bossy with him.

In 1897 he went to St. Paul's Preparatory School as a first-former, and Minnie was so worried about him you would have thought he was being sent into Outer Mongolia. She filled the poor boy's head with so much cautionary advice he couldn't have moved a step if he had remembered and followed it all. Of course, everything went very well for him and we got enthusiastic letters full of stories about football, skating and sledding.

Then came 1898, a year of great importance in my story, because it was then that your mother and father met, but I will save my description of that until the next chapter. I want to review the next five years in my mind before I start to write. There is so much to tell that it needs a lot of sorting out to put it in the proper order.

Before I start telling you about your mother and father from the time they met, let me go back and tell you some of the things I know about your father's early life that your grandfather may not have related to you. We talked a lot about it, he and I, and I got more from your mother after he died.

Did you know that your father was born in Nahant, not Boston, in the summer house that your grandparents bought soon after they were married?

When your Greenough grandparents married, your grandfather was traveling a lot for his employer, the Boston Gas Company, so rather than set up housekeeping in Boston with a town house, your grandmother lived in Worcester in the winter and in the Nahant house during the summer. When your grandfather was in Boston for a time, they had a "flat" in the first apartment house in America, the Pelham Hotel. This worked out very well until your uncles and aunts came along. Then, for two years, they rented the house at 16 West Cedar Street on Beacon Hill until they bought the house on the corner of Chestnut and West Cedar Streets.

This was where they all grew up and, although it was sold before your mother and father met, quite coincidentally I was in it many years later at a dinner party given by the then owner, so I can describe it quite well.

It was an enormous house compared with the previous one at 16 West Cedar, four stories high with a sixty foot frontage on Chestnut Street and about twenty-two on West Cedar. You entered by a door at street level on West Cedar Street and went through a vestibule into a long front hall with two fireplaces on the Chestnut Street wall to the left. Standing against the opposite wall was a lovely white bannistered, mahogany railed staircase sweeping up in a graceful curve to the left from the front hall landing to the second floor. The front hall itself, with white woodwork and a light rose wallpaper, was a bright area when the sun was out, having five windows on the long wall to the south and one large one looking out on West Cedar.

At the far end of the front hall a set of three stairs rose to a reception room with chairs and tables grouped around a small fireplace on the interior wall. Beyond, at the very back of the house, was the back door and stairs leading up to the floors above and down to the basement where the kitchen and servants' dining room were located.

The drawing room was on the second floor over the front hall, with two large green marble-faced fireplaces on the Chestnut Street wall and a repetition of the same window pattern on the floor below. Beyond the drawing room, over the reception room, were the dining room and the butler's pantry where a dumbwaiter descended to the cellar kitchen.

I have always found it easy to reconstruct the pattern of life that a house implies, especially if I know something about the occupants. This is how I imagine it was when your father was growing up.

First of all, it was a fine location. The house was within easy walking distance of the Gas Company's offices, and the nearby Common and Public Garden provided a wonderful playground for all the neighborhood children. As there were many families of similar background living close by that the Greenoughs knew, the children were never at a loss to find companions to play with. Your grandfather's beloved Somerset Club was just up the hill on Beacon Street, there were convenient shops, and a good Italian grocery store called "DeLuca's" had opened up recently down on Charles Street.

Beacon Hill was especially delightful at Christmas time when, after a good snowfall, the whole hill took on the look of Dickens's London. Christmas trees were set in living room windows, and the curtains were left open so that passers-by were treated to the glittering splendor of ornaments and myriads of small candles perched in their branches. In basement windows there were candle-lit nativity scenes, known locally as "crèches," adding other, smaller jewels of colored light, so that the whole south side of Beacon Hill glowed richly in the dark with these presentations. If St. Nicholas flew over, the whole Hill must have looked like a huge Christmas tree, with each house window a decoration on it.

During January and February it was bitterly cold, and the wind gained an even crueler velocity as it blew up Chestnut Street from the Charles River. Waking in the still dark morning, your father could tell by sound and smell if it had snowed during the night. The muffled sound of the horses' hooves, the snow crunching under the carriage wheels, the screek-screek of the handyman's scraper as he pushed it over the sidewalk bricks to clear them, told the story. He could tell by his nose too, by that smell that snow gives to city air, cleaning it for a time of all its odors.

Winter was a time for reading aloud. In the afternoon your grandmother Lizzie would gather her children in the little third-floor sitting room, whose two small windows looked out over the rooftops of the houses lower down the hill to the bleak, ice-covered Charles River. With the children sprawled on sofas or floor in front of the fireplace, she read from Howard Pyle's "Robin Hood" or "Men Of Iron," "Little Lord Fauntleroy," or your father's favorite "Page, Squire, and Knight: a Romance of the Days of Chivalry." On many a dark winter afternoon, with sleet rattling on the windows, the little room would be transformed into summertime in Sherwood Forest with the sun shining through the trees on Robin and his merry men.

Finally came long-awaited spring with melting snow on the brick sidewalks and water gurgling in the gutters. The sun was suddenly warm and promising, and the wind, having lost its bite, was as intoxicating as wine. The sky above the dark rooflines was bright blue, warmed by the higher angle of the sun and cut here and there with swift-flying, wind-blown wisps of chimney smoke. Winter sports were forgotten in an instant. No more sledding on the Boston Common or skating on the Frog Pond; the wooden sleds with their iron clad runners, the clamp-on skates, and moth-balled boxes of winter woolens were sent to summer oblivion in the cellar.

Then suddenly it was June and time for your grandmother Lizzie and the children to open the house in Nahant, see to the repair of winter storm damage, and prepare for the visiting friends and relatives that were the obligatory guests of the owner of a summer house. Those first days of summer in Nahant were very special to your father. He told me how alive and vital he felt when he woke to the unexpected sound of waves lapping on the rocks and the pungent smell of seaweed. There was the great pleasure of building a crude "boat" out of an old crate and then experiencing the thrill of precariously floating in it on the water of some little cove, with crabs and small fish scuttling below.

However, the Greenoughs did not spend the whole summer in Nahant. Your grandfather had plenty of vacation time, and he liked to divide his summer holidays between several resorts. Part of the summer they would be in Nahant and he would commute to Boston on the steamboat. Then the family would relocate for four to six weeks, and he would join them for as much time as he could spare. As his great sporting pleasure was sailing, their vacation spots tended to be ocean-oriented. They often spent a month or so in Maine at summer hotels or they would visit your great uncle Charlie in his big shingled, weather-beaten house at West Chop on Martha's Vineyard.

When it came to education, your father's and his siblings' early years in Boston were like those of most others of their social position in the Back Bay. Your father went to school at Boston Latin, then prepped for college at Mr. Hopkinson's School at 29 Chestnut Street (known to all students as "Hoppy's"). Later, when the family moved to Cleveland in 1892, he transferred to the University School in that city. From what I have heard, he was an average student whose main problem was an inability to pay attention in class.

He was an extraordinarily handsome boy in quite a different style from the other males of the Greenough family who, though not at all unhandsome, were far less finely constructed. Sister Ethel shared his chiseled good looks in a feminine fashion, while Charles and Eugenia were more in the traditionally craggy Greenough mold.

Greenough males were generally on the short side, with small heads, large protruding ears, and slightly beaked noses. Your father was somewhat taller with a larger head and flatter ears. His nose was straight, and his eyes were dark and deep set. His hands were long and elegant. In fact his whole appearance was "elegant." Your aunt Eugenia, as a little girl, once said of her brother Malcolm, "He looks like an angel, but he probably isn't."

In the summer of 1892, when your grandfather Greenough accepted an appointment as the general manager of the Cleveland Gas Company, he sold the Chestnut Street house, bought a house at 724 Euclid Avenue in Cleveland, and moved there in the fall of 1892. This was not an appealing move for your father, who felt, with some justification, that Cleveland was a crude middlewestern town. He was a bit of a snob (though not obnoxiously so) and longed to return to "The East."

Two years later, his wish was granted when he was accepted as a Harvard freshman in the class of 1898. He arrived there on a sunny September morning in 1894 with all his trunks and boxes, the dirt and grime of the train ride from Cleveland still clinging to his clothes. He settled into his rooms in suite 38 at Ware Hall with his cousin Frazier Curtis from Manchester, Massachusetts, whose first communication to Malcolm was to inform him that he owed $119.75 for his half of the annual rental, including services such as daily cleaning, and fresh linens, of course. Isn't that incredible — it must cost four times that much today!

Frazier Curtis was very prominent in the club life of Harvard. He belonged to almost all of them and was an officer of many. He had tremendous energy and an engaging personality, and soon became a real leader of his class. I met and talked to him a number of times. I thought he was going to go out and conquer the world, but unfortunately he developed an obsessive hatred for the Jewish race and was quite paranoiac in many other ways as well. Still, he was a fascinating man when I knew him in his early days. Your father joined quite a number of clubs himself: the Glee Club, the Banjo and Mandolin Club, the Signet Club, the Phi Delta Psi, the Hasty Pudding Club, the Lampoon, the Fencing Club, and the Golf Club. (From reading your yearbook I see you have done just as well.)

Your father used to row on the Charles River in a small boat called a "wherry." He often told the story of how one day he tipped over opposite M.I.T. and tried to swim the wherry ashore. He swam and pushed and swam and pushed until he was so exhausted he could no longer even hold onto the boat. He slipped off, thinking he was about to drown, and sank down into the water. He only sank about three feet before he found himself sitting on the bottom. He was embarrassed to find out that he could have walked the whole way in from where he had capsized!

Did you know that he was a director of the Harvard Lampoon and wrote many pieces for its weekly publication? He and his classmate R.P. Utter, the class day orator, wrote the lyrics for the Hasty Pudding Show "Boscabello." Your father played the part of Suzette, the French nurse — "Chic, but no chicken," as the playbill stated.

His course grades were not very impressive. However, a gentlemanly C average was no disgrace in those days either among the students, parents, or prospective employers. The important thing was for a boy to participate in "college life," to build friendships among his fellow students, and to be inspired by the faculty to do at least a small amount of academic work. Harvard College was one large club, a lifelong fraternity whose members stood up for one another in times of need. The Harvard final clubs added the further element of an inner circle within an inner circle. To be a Harvard man set one apart; to be a Harvard club man was to be one of the élitest of the élite.

When your father graduated from Harvard in June of 1898, his future was determined. All he had to do was to follow the prescribed course. He was to take the summer off, vacationing at Nahant, and later go with the family to spend a month at the Marshall House at York Harbor, Maine. After that, he would escort his mother and sisters back to Cleveland and begin his career as an apprentice in the Cleveland Gas Company's training program for young executive candidates.

But this was all in the future for your father. He hadn't thought about it very deeply. At the moment the pleasant summer just ahead held most of his attention.

Malcolm W. Greenough
89 Marlborough Street
Boston, Mass.

December 12, 1925

Dear Aunt Lily,

Not having heard from you in over a month, I was quite worried about you until I talked to Uncle Atwood on the phone the other day. He said he had heard from you recently and that you were fine, and gave me your new address.

We have some wonderful news! Kathleen is pregnant and will have the baby in June if everyone's calculations are right. Isn't that swell!

I am hoping for a boy, of course, and I already have the forms in hand to enroll him in Groton and Harvard the minute he's born. There will be another Greenough boy playing football for you to worry about, your great grandnephew Malcolm Whelen Greenough, Jr.

Also, I haven't received any more of the family history that you are writing; I hope that it hasn't gone astray in the mail or that you haven't gotten tired of the job, because you have been doing so well, and Katsy and I are both fascinated by it all.

The last batch that you sent us finished off by telling about Uncle Charlie Whelen and you were just about to describe how Mother and Father met in 1898, and, naturally, I'm very anxious to hear about that.

Write soon, or call me collect here at home (COMmonwealth 4325).

Lots of love,
Mally

ST. CHARLES HOTEL
3915 St. Charles Street
New Orleans, La.

December 18, 1925

Dear Mally,

I am so sorry to cause you concern, and so touched that you should worry about this old Southern lady. What wonderful news though! My congratulations to you both. It would be just fine if he is a boy, but a little girl would be very nice too.

It's quite true, I haven't been writing for some time. I don't know if it's just the Christmas blues that seem to affect me more each year, or the pain I know I will experience when I finally come face to face with telling the story of the intertwining of your parents' lives — first so beautiful and then so tragic. For me to write about that is going to be like climbing a mountain. I guess I have been trying to build up my strength for the effort.

I'll start again after New Year's. Give my especial love to Kathleen and tell her I will write her soon.

A Merry Christmas and a Happy New Year to you all and my best regards to your mother-in-law, Mrs. Parkman,* and to your grandfather.

Much love to you all,
Aunt Lily

---

* *Author's note:* Kathleen's widowed mother, Mrs. Abbot Lawrence Rotch, married Mr. Henry Parkman, Jr. in November 1919.

ST. CHARLES HOTEL
3915 St. Charles Street
New Orleans, La.

January 11, 1926

Dear Mally,

Well, I finally got over my Christmas blues, or whatever it was, screwed up my courage, and started writing again last Sunday afternoon. It wasn't easy, getting started, but as I went on I was so swept along by the emotion of it all that I couldn't stop. I kept at it for three days straight, only taking time out to eat and sleep, in an obsession to get it done.

Then I rested up for a day and spent the rest of the week going over it and making corrections, because I made a lot of mistakes in my rush. I hope that you (and especially your secretary) can make it out all right.

Even though it's messy, I do think it came out well. I hope you agree.

Much love as always,
Aunt Lily

Chapter 14

It was the dinner hour at the Marshall House Hotel at the little seaside town of York, Maine. We had arrived by coastal steamer that afternoon and had had barely enough time to unpack and get down in time to be served. Resort hotels required more punctuality at meals then than they do now.

After two days of hard traveling in the early July heat, Minnie, your mother, Charlie Jr. and I were all looking forward to our first meal at the hotel. Most of the other guests had been seated when we entered the enormous white dining room with its large windows letting in the wonderfully refreshing, salt-scented breezes from the Atlantic. As we stepped into the dining room, we were pleased to note that the people seated around their tables in their formal evening wear looked sophisticated enough to reassure us that we had not made a mistake in selecting this hotel.

As the very French-appearing maître d'hôtel was leading us to our table, I noticed an extremely handsome young man staring at your mother with a look of wonder in his expression that seemed to say he had never seen anyone quite like her before. Your mother was facing in his direction as she sat down, and I saw their eyes meet for a moment and her quick warm smile at him before she turned to answer a question from Minnie. All during the meal they were making surreptitious appraisals of each other. It was very amusing.

After dinner we all retired to the sitting room where, as was the custom, we were presented to the other guests there. Among these was the Malcolm Scollay Greenough family of Boston: father, mother, daughters Ethel and Eugenia, and a most anxious son — your father,

Malcolm Junior, eager to be introduced but quite tongue-tied in the event.

A corner of the wide veranda that surrounded the hotel had been cordonned off for dancing and decorated with Chinese candle-lanterns. A small orchestra began to play, and soon dancing couples could be seen through the windows of the sitting room as they glided back and forth, first in candlelight and then in silhouette against the moonlit sea beyond.

The orchestra began a waltz, and your father asked your mother to dance. She accepted and he led her out onto the floor, moving to an advantageous position to begin, and held out his arms. She stepped into them and they whirled off without hesitation as if they had danced together all their lives. They were clearly the best dancers on the floor and, content for the moment with the pleasure of their performance, they danced in comfortable silence, feeling direction and response through their white-gloved hands.

When the dance ended, they took glasses of punch from the refreshment table and withdrew to a corner of the porch where they began to talk. As Violett reported later, they asked the usual questions strangers ask, yet seemed to have already achieved a state of intimacy that made the answers almost the expected ones. It was as though they were new and old friends all at once. In fact they were more than friends, that they knew, but what they couldn't say; they could not have described their feelings at that moment if they tried.

From that moment on, they were inseparable. I would see them in their boating clothes leaving in a state of high excitement for a canoe trip up the river to picnic on some grassy bank. Then I would see them again, returning at sunset all aglow with the sun and the recollection of their adventures. Long before they reached the hotel landing I could hear your mother's voice carrying clear far across the reddened waters as she sang to your father while he guided their canoe home.

Often, of an afternoon, they would walk out along the headland to view the ocean crashing against the rocks below, surging up and sucking back, with the hard gargling sound of countless small stones rolling slowly back to sea only to be hurled swiftly up again.

From the hotel porch, I could see their distant figures standing at the cliff edge as they paused to ignore for a moment the beauties of nature and contemplate each other. With the wind ruffling their clothes, they stood face to face — she with her closed parasol over her shoulder, holding her dress close to thwart the breeze, and he with cloth cap pressed down tight, the tail of his belted Norfolk jacket whipping out behind him, and his stick held at the same jaunty angle over his shoulder as her parasol.

One would talk, the other smile and reply, both laugh and then lean close to share some intimate remark, pause thus in silence for a moment, and then link arms and walk on down the cliffside path. How beautiful and bittersweet it was for me to see them like that from my solitary chair on the hotel veranda. But such moments of jealousy and self pity were short-lived. I was far too happy for them to let my own selfish feelings spoil it.

They were continually on the go. Tennis (your father liked it less than your mother), sailing (your father was an expert, your mother an eager novice), riding (both were moderately competent), walking and canoeing made up the list of their activities.

Then, too, York Harbor contributed a most delightful setting for the birth of their love affair. Let me describe it for you.

The Marshall House Hotel, then about ten years old, was situated on a high rocky island barely connected to the mainland by a narrow causeway between the harbor at York village and the York River at a point just before the river joins the Atlantic Ocean. The building was rectangular, with one long side facing southeast, running parallel to the edge of the channel between the river and the sea. A wide, covered porch some fifty feet above the water ran around all four sides of the hotel on a level with the first floor, with many of the public rooms opening directly onto it. On the hottest summer days these rooms were dark and cool — quiet, secluded, usually deserted inner spaces filled with a shadowy peace. Gentle breezes stirred the draperies, and the sunlit world outside made the windows seem like brilliant pictures on the dark walls.

At night these same rooms were bright and bustling, soft gaslight reflecting from mirrors and white-painted woodwork — alive with the hum of conversations, the muted noise of busy waiters moving back and forth between kitchen and table, and the sound of music from the orchestra in the ballroom or on the porch.

To the southwest the hotel had a fine view of the York River curving behind Harris and Bragdon Islands. Tea was served on this section of the piazza in the late afternoon so that the guests could enjoy the often spectacular sunsets over land and water. It was from this high vantage point that we would see the canoeists returning from their excursions up river.

On the northwest side, the hotel looked down on the harbor and the little coastal village of York with its long pier running out into the water from the end of Simpson's Lane. Here coastal steamers struggled up against the tidal bore to pick up and leave off passengers on one of their many stops between Boston and Bar Harbor. Travel by sea was very popular with summer vacationers then; it gave them a head start on their holiday to escape immediately from the city dock to the cool, windy deck of a passenger ship.

From the northeast side of the hotel there was a magnificent view of the Atlantic Ocean, unspoiled by any sign of human habitation. Only boats under sail or oar and the occasional steamboat broke the vast panoramic emptiness. This was what people came to Maine for. Everyone then believed that to bathe in the ocean waters and breathe the salty air blowing over them had medicinal effects that were almost magical. The more boldly a resort hotel stood out into the Atlantic, the better. Therefore the Marshall House with its high position and water on three sides was one of the most popular.

Boardwalks and stairways led from the hotel porch down to piers, which in turn were connected by gangways to floats on the southwest and southeast sides of the building. Around these floats were tied a variety of small boats and canoes available to the hotel guests, and at all times of the day there was a constant coming and going.

On the northwest side, where the wide piazza was interrupted by the main entrance to the hotel, was a long, gently inclined graveled road leading down to the causeway and the town, providing easy access from the hotel to Harbor Beach on the Atlantic side of the causeway, where there were bath houses for those who wished to swim. Nearby, a tennis court was marked out on the grass, and on almost any afternoon when it wasn't too breezy, there would be players there and a good gallery of guests to cheer them on.

Aside from the village and a few scattered houses and farms inland, it was a sparsely occupied, unspoiled rural area. No telephone poles, wires, or billboards then marred the streets or roads. No noisy automobiles competed with the soft sounds of wind through trees and grass, of water burbling against rock and river's edge, or the harsh, lonely cry of a seagull gliding overhead. Under the warm summer's sun, your parents were as alone on their trips up river or walks around the headland as Adam and Eve in their unspoiled garden.

The weather was exceptionally fine that summer, even by the most demanding standards. To your parents it must have seemed like paradise to have that lovely setting and such perfect weather. In one of his letters your father said how the meadows above the river were "as the poet said, 'bee-loud and flower-scented, water-lapped and wind-caressed.' " Even the few rainy days were wonderful to them, the foghorn as sweet and stirring as a cello and the seaweed-scented fog a rich perfume.

They were so new to each other, and they had so much to say, so much to ask. Each fresh disclosure created a new delight to share or mystery to explore together. There seemed never to be a false step, a serious difference of opinion, a disappointing flaw found in the other.

For instance, they discovered they shared an almost druid-like worship of trees. Lofty elms inspired them, gnarled and twisted oaks reminded them of goblins and sprites in the fairy tales of their youth, a stand of willows by the riverbank seemed like a group of green-skirted ballerinas dancing in place.

Their favorite tree at York was an enormous beech that stood in a large grassy meadow beyond the village. Its silvered double trunks twisted up, joining and parting until they vanished high above in the dense copper-colored leaves. What birds or other secret things nested up there, they wondered. What fun it would be to climb up and lie there hidden from the world below.

At the base of the tree, large, gray, finger-like roots reached out and sank into the damp earth, sometimes crossing over one another to form little basins that caught and held rainwater for the birds to drink. One long low branch forked some distance from the trunk, providing them with two gently swaying seats where they would sit and talk, shaded from the sun and sheltered from the world.

You may wonder how I can write so knowledgeably about these private matters. It is because they were both very close to me, and at one time or another I heard it all from their own lips. Little is more precious to me than their inclusion of me in these confidences. Then, too, after their deaths I came into possession of many of the letters your mother received from your father. I have kept them for you all these years. Some contain beautiful descriptions of their times together that summer, which I will quote from a little later.

Time that summer proceeded at its normal pace for us mortals, but for your mother and father it sped by as fast as the York River rushing past them to the sea. All too soon there were yellow-brown leaves in the stream and the summer was over.

As I mentioned earlier, your father was to start his training at the Cleveland Gas Company that fall, so the Greenoughs left the sixth of September, and the Whelen party two days later. We made a stopover in Boston to see your mother back for her third year at Dana Hall and, at the same time, put young Charlie on a train to Concord, New Hampshire, for his second-form year at St. Paul's.

That done, Minnie and I boarded the train to Philadelphia at Back Bay Station and settled into our compartment for the long trip home. Your grandmother started to read and then turned to me and said, "You don't suppose Violett is seriously interested in that Greenough boy, do you?"

I replied, "In all frankness Minnie, I do, but I don't think she knows it yet."

"I think you're wrong," she said. "It was just a summer crush; it will fade away to a sweet memory by the first snowfall."

"Perhaps, perhaps," I answered, and we both went back to our books.

The day the Greenoughs left York was dismally cold with fog and rain. Even though the steamer wasn't due to depart for quite some time, your grandfather took the rest of the family down to the boat landing immediately after lunch. He always had a horror of being late for things. Your father took your mother out on the porch despite the weather to have a little privacy for their farewells. He describes it so well in one of his letters to your mother that I will quote it here instead of describing the scene myself:

> . . . Do you know, I remember the day we parted, every single second till the last, as if it was yesterday, and I can see that bare, desolate piazza stretching away, chill and damp

into vistas of drifting mist and fog and rain. You had on a light blue dress, and wore a red rose. We walked around [the hotel] once and then, when I felt as if something in me was being torn shred by shred, all I could do was say "Goodbye" and touch your hand a second, just a second, and go. I can see you now just as plainly as I did then. You looked sorry too, dear friend, for we had merry times, but you couldn't know the way I felt — as if I was about to be transported for a crime . . .

After saying goodbye your father walked down the long path past the beach where they had gone swimming. The small beach stones were rattling back and forth in the surge and gulls were crying above as they had on sunnier days, but the summer smell had gone. Now there was a cold, raw scent of salt and seaweed and a whiff of woodsmoke from a chimney in the village.

With heavy heart he continued on down the granite steps to the ferry landing to join his waiting family on the steamer taking them back to Boston. Feeling too melancholy to talk, he excused himself and went to stand alone in the stern and think about all the things he would liked to have said to your mother before they parted if only he had been quick enough to think of them at the time. As the boat churned its way through the misty waters, he leaned on the rail, looking up as they passed below the high, dark bulk of the hotel. Too soon it was lost in the fog and gloom, and he thought of your mother with a lump in his throat and wondered when he would ever see her again and whether it would ever be the same. Could there ever again be a summer like the one just passed? Could someone as lovely as your mother possibly love him as he loved her?

Back in her snug room at the Marshall House, your mother was abstractedly preparing for dinner and thinking of your father and that farewell scene on the piazza. There were things she would have liked to have said too. If your father could have known how much she was thinking about him at that moment, he would have worried far less.

Chapter 15

From what they told me later, your mother and father had barely finished unpacking before they began to correspond. In the most delicate terms and restrained phrases they started to define their feelings for each other, saying all those things left unspoken at York.

A month or so passed and then suddenly out of the blue, or so it seemed to me, Minnie announced that we were all going abroad for the winter and perhaps longer. The reasons she gave were as follows. Young Charlie had collapsed on the athletic field at St. Paul's School and was thought to have injured his heart. His doctors had prescribed a prolonged rest. Minnie herself had been in ill health and could not face the cold Philadelphia winter. Finally, she felt that your mother would benefit more from time spent abroad than at Dana Hall. Those were her public reasons, but I think that they were greatly augmented by the fact that observing the constant flow of mail between your parents, she had become a little alarmed, believing that her daughter was too young to become so involved with one man no matter how nice he was.

Like many society mothers of those days, she had plans for your mother. She wanted to introduce her to society not only in Philadelphia and New York, but also abroad in London, Paris and Rome. She felt certain that Violett would attract many proposals and be able to make what was then called "a brilliant match." Indeed Minnie probably felt that she would be remiss in her duties as a mother if she did not give her daughter such an opportunity. She had originally planned to wait until the next year to go abroad, but your father's appearance on the scene persuaded her to accelerate her schedule.

There was a great rush of buying and packing, hastily made travel arrangements, and collecting your mother and young Charlie from their schools. Finally, all was assembled on the dock in Hoboken, New Jersey, where the new German liner "Bismarck" was due to depart on November 17th, 1898.

We barely made it; they were almost pulling in the gangway as we ascended it, but at last we were aboard with all our belongings. The ship's horn bellowed, the engines made the whole ship shudder with their efforts to separate us from the dock, and then we were steaming out of the harbor past the Statue of Liberty, which remained in view for some time until the shoreline disappeared behind us, and we were alone on the broad Atlantic headed for Europe.

My feelings about that trip were confused. On the one hand I had planned never to "cross the waters" again; I had no wish to put temptation in my way as far as William was concerned, but your mother had pleaded with me so earnestly to come that I could not refuse her. She had guessed, I am sure, Minnie's intentions and, sensing my unspoken admiration of your father, saw in me someone she could turn to if she found herself in need of comfort or advice. As things turned out she never availed herself of my counsel then, but I am glad I went anyway.

Our plan was to sail directly to Naples, go from there to Rome and then to Venice. After Venice we would go through the Simplon Pass to Switzerland, and spend some time in the Bernese Alps, move on to Germany and eventually to France. The final leg of the journey was to England, but I intended to excuse myself at that time on some pretext and return home directly from France. (The best-laid plans etc. . . .)

Despite a report of terrific winter gales and snow around the British Isles, our crossing was uneventful. Fortunately the bad weather did not extend as far south as our course so we were in no danger.

In Naples we stayed at the Bristol, a very modern hotel lit entirely by electricity. We had a lovely view of the bay over the rooftops and our rooms were furnished with yellow damask draperies and handsome rosewood furniture. The weather was sunny and warm and our prospects seemed most pleasant.

During the trip across your mother seemed to undergo a sudden and remarkable metamorphosis. Whereas in Philadelphia she would continually bring your father's name into the conversation or refer to some adventure they had shared, she now stopped talking about your father entirely. "Well," I thought, "perhaps Minnie was right after all." But I underestimated her. As I later found out, she had decided that the best tactic for her to adopt was one of outward indifference to your father, and she played her part so well that she fooled us all.

In Naples we joined forces with Minnie's sister-in-law Laura Whelen and her daughter Elsie. They had reached Naples a week earlier and on learning of our arrival and itinerary conformed their plans to ours so that we could be together the whole time we were abroad.

We had many delightful little adventures worth recounting. On a coach ride up the Posillipo your mother exclaimed about a beautiful clump of roses growing over the top of a high wall; our gallant little Neapolitan driver placed our coach under them, and, by standing on tiptoe, managed to pluck one rose, which he presented to her with a courtly bow. If you look in the scrapbook she kept of the trip, you will find it there along with a hundred other mementoes.

At another time, we lunched at a café where ladies sat alone at tables smoking cigarettes with their demi-tasses while men in the back of the room sang passionate Italian love songs. The place had a wonderfully "sinful" atmosphere.

We traveled to Pompei and took the railway up to the summit of Vesuvius. All the drama of that catastrophic night two millenia ago lay at our feet. It was very impressive. A week later we went to Amalfi, where your mother celebrated her eighteenth birthday by taking a donkey ride with Charlie and Elsie around the steep cliffside paths.

On our way to Rome we stopped at lovely little Sorrento and purchased some of its famous stockings, then proceeded on to the Eternal City, where we settled into the Hotel d'Angleterre for a long stay.

As I said, your mother was keeping her own counsel about your father. She said little of him in public, but her scrapbook of the trip tells a different story. By its testimony she lived in an inner frenzy of impatience for his letters which she pasted in it with little comments underneath such as "At long last!" or "More intoxicating than champagne!"

His letters took her back to their time together in York and kept it vivid in her mind. Indeed, they are so well done that I will quote from them here.

He starts by describing his apprenticeship at the Cleveland Gas Company:

My foot is well and I am at work again. If you had only seen the dainty Malcolm Scollay Greenough, Junior, Esquire, A.B., in a hole, in a muddy street, in a pipe, in overalls, caulking a joint with rope, and an Irishman, you would have felt like [taking] a picture . . . For all of this my heart is in the right place. Be sure to take good care of it in your travels, and you must pay duty on it just as often as you can and let me see the bills of possession in writing very, very often . . .

Do I remember all those lovely things? Do I remember my name? Can't I reminisce too? Do you remember the night we canoed down the river after the picnic, where all we could see was the inky waters beneath the dark fringes of the whispering trees on the banks, and the steely glitter of the stars, and each other?

Do you remember how we just drifted and swept, and slipped down, down, down with the phosphorescence gleaming in two silver ribbons, while we talked and talked and you sang "Beauty's Eyes"? These and countless (nay! counted) other times; the Tennyson Sunday, the drive we had the night of the fireworks and the dances — think how much they are to me now . . .

Remember then all these things, and be most sure that the spirit that held us together last summer, and prompted the unburdening of our souls, and all the good I got from you, must be something real; and that the letters that you write me from the world where once I was, and lived, bring with them the embodiment of all this goodness, and help me.

Of my present life there is little of interest. I go to the works, to the laboratory, to dinner, to the theatre, and then do the same the next day. There are no men I know, and what girls I play with are here only temporarily and then off East again. East, oh, that place, where all is civilized, and refined, and as I have always known things to be done — it is so far away. So if my letters are uninteresting, remember my environment, and trust in the knowledge that you are helping a friend.

Your true friend ever,
Malcolm Scollay Greenough, Jr.

In his next letter, dated November 9th, he wrote:

> I'm being made to order now, and in a few years I shall be a finished product labeled "Gas Engineer." . . . My life as an engineer is new I must admit, and it must needs be mechanical and sordid and hard in this first drudgery. But when I sit beside a whirling, powerful machine and all the air about crashes and clangs with the rattle and roar of iron broken to man's will — strong, hard, oily, sooty man, virile and earnest in his work — I can think that there was a time I could lie prone upon a grassy bank beside the great slipping river and look far across the sunlit fields to the warm blue sky. Or, turning, look up into your face, to chat or laugh and so to fill God's glorious summer days with all that was sweet and good in its intimacy with the summer world and each other, until twilight swept us down into the dark to say goodbye there, though only for a few short hours.
>
> But now, I am afraid, dear friend, that even your sweet plan for next year [to meet again in Maine the following summer], so far away as it seems to you, will be but at the beginning of the job for which my present work is as training. It will be more time than that before I earn the right to stop a bit, but it is just these thoughts of being with you again that can help me now, and when you write to me, and tell me you still remember all these things, then I know that all this is worthwhile . . .

In another letter Malcolm said:

> Do you remember how you saved my life last summer after I was ill? And the pipe you procured with Natty, and how we used to smoke it in the little cottage by the sea? And

the drive? I remember every word you said. You gave me a kiss, and we let the old horse walk for miles on that quiet peaceful road under the trees. Then we came home under the sunset and you took the picture on the old bridge.

Later in the same letter he refers to a boat ride they took in York Harbor:

> . . . Oh, what bully sunsets we did see! Old Sol hasn't set since, that is I don't think he has, I haven't noticed, but he used to set then, yes, and we'd come sliding down with the tide. I'd say, "Let her drift, we've got time to burn," and so we would, and you'd sing until we could see the lights of the Marshall House shining out across the bay. I'd never care what time it was, or what happened just so long as it lasted! Ah! Those were the days! And now you're in Rome and I'm in Cleveland, neither of which is York . . .

In the next letter, he recalls:

> Our day! I never think of it without a smile. We couldn't decide what to do, and finally we paddled across the river and went up the road, and every place we struck that seemed nice was hot or cold, with mosquitoes thicker than taxes, until finally we found a rock for you to lean against and then it rained great guns! My word, I was peevish with that weather. Funny, funny time!
>
> There isn't any news. McKinley is still president and Mark [Hanna] and I do what we can to keep things going. Hobson is still being kissed, and the Maine is still remembered, thanks be. The world still goes around, and if you will write me soon, perhaps I can stay on it, and pray that my part will stay still, 'til yours moves around to it again.

Your father wrote very well, I think. I hope his descriptions are as vivid to you as they are to me. I have never found your mother's replies, but from your father's references to them I know they echoed his sentiments about their experiences during the summer of '98.

———

Chapter 16

We stayed in Rome for two months and did all the tourist things — the catacombs, the Colosseum, etc., but we also enjoyed the pleasures of society, so plentiful in that city. Minnie and Charles had been there before and had many friends who took great pains to entertain us in their homes and to "show us around."

One such friend was Mr. Ezekiel, an artist with wild blue eyes and long white hair and beard, who had a charming studio near the Baths of Diocletian. He frightened me at first because he reminded me so forcefully of that strange person with the scythe I had seen as a little girl in New Orleans, but his manner was so gentle and considerate I soon forgot the resemblance. He gave a Christmas party for the poor children of the area that we attended. I shall never forget all those ragged little urchins crowded at the base of that huge Christmas tree in that white, marble-walled studio.

Two American gentlemen soon appeared to pay court to your mother. Reginald S. Huidekoper was a small, dark-complected, suave New Yorker. A bit untidy in his dress, he was addicted to wearing a bowler hat he had acquired in England (he was a Rhodes Scholar at Oxford at the time), to smoking countless cigarettes and to making the most atrocious puns I have ever heard in my life. He was almost too outspoken, but for all that he was a delightful person and a great addition to our company. He and your mother got on extremely well — so well, in fact, that I fear he misunderstood her feelings for him.

Garrett Pier, also a New Yorker, was the antithesis of Mr. Huidekoper. Very tall, blond, impeccably stylish in his dress, he was thought shy by some and overly reserved by others. He was in fact merely quiet and undemonstrative and, though he was a great athlete, he never spoke of his accomplishments except to young Charlie, who idolized him and pestered the details out of him. From Charlie I heard about Mr. Pier's prowess at rowing, football, golf, tennis, fishing, hunting, and, although it was not a sport, his passion for photography. Later, I chanced to mention his name to a knowledgeable man, who told me that Pier was indeed first class in several sports, good enough in fact to be asked to participate in the recently revived Olympic Games, but that he had no ambitions along that line, disliking publicity as much as he did.

Count Luigi Primoli was an Italian gentleman much taken with your mother, though she had to share his affections with the two other loves in his life — his food and himself. Never was there a greater egotist or anyone who spouted such a profusion of self-praising superlatives. The perfect example of this was the dinner menu he sent around with each of his invitations. (Actually they were more like summonses.) Besides the bill of fare, each invitation included a picture of the count poetically posed on a ducal chair, sitting on one foot with his forefinger tip to his chin as if to say, "Look at me — I'm as delectable a morsel as the meal itself!" He was a perfect buffoon, but I must say his meals were delicious.

I think it must have been Violett's tales of Count Luigi in her letters to your father that inspired a poem that he sent back to her. It went as follows:

A ROMANZA

They met one day in the summer time
In a village by the sea
She was a maiden passing fair
Lovely young man was he!

And all through that summer
Their friendship grew
They canoed and sailed and danced
It is not known his effect on her
He was simply entranced!

She sweetly said to him one day
As by the sea they sat —

"I'm going abroad, to marry a lord
Now what do you think of that?"

Ho! Ho! he laughed, Ha, Ha, he laughed
You'd better stick with me,
I'm going to work, and get
As rich as I can be.

Hee! Hee! she laughed, I'd have to wait
About ninety years she said
To live in the palace I want with you,
His will be ready made.

So off she sailed this little maid
To distant Italy
And there she met Ricardo Phillippo,
Cubre Liber, Castellones de Cordova,
The Count of Spaghetti

Oh rapturous gurrl, Oh be my love!
We will never part again,
So off she went a Vicontess
To his castle in sunny Spain

But it was a castle in Spain all right
With a mortgage on the top,
And after a year they came over here
To start a barber shop.

The poem concludes by describing how a well dressed stranger
comes in for a shave and has so much gold that "the money ran out of his
boots." After shaving off the man's beard and getting paid ten dollars,
the barber calls in his wife, who recognizes our hero, lets out a shriek,
tears out her hair, grinds her teeth and bites a tree in her vexation.

"There now," wrote your father, "look at that and tremble! . . . If
you don't like your fate you can avoid it . . . !"

He continued:

It was awfully sweet of you, dear friend, to think of me in
Tivoli, and I only wish I were there with you. Your card is in

my glass, your pin is in my tie, and my gurrl can do no wrong.
Please think of me every little while, and I hope you like this
letter better, and write soon —

> As ever,
> *Greenberg*

While I'm quoting your father's poetry there's another that I find
so touching I'll include it here even though it may be somewhat out of
place. It was in a letter he wrote her in late January, 1899. He said:

. . . Although you probably won't get this anywhere near
Valentine's Day, what's the odds so long as you get it, and the
lyric is not lost to the language.

A VALENTINE

The thing to do about this time,
Or so most people think
Is write a pretty Valentine,
And make it rhyme with "you're divine"
Say "I'll be yours and you be mine"
And will you be my Valentine?
Till driven nigh to drink.

But now to you it's perfect bliss
To pen a lyric true
For you are now in distant Rome,
Which rhymes with very far from home,
And friends who hope you soon will come,
Again to those you parted from,
Truly from me to you. (From me to you)

And so I guess I'll simply say,
Just as I like to talk,
My happy days I spent with thee.
By gliding stream, 'neath shady tree,
Shall mark through all eternity,
A friendship made most dear to me,
A month with thee at York.

M.S.G., Jr.

Rome was followed by Florence, then Venice, over the Alps to Switzerland, and finally down into warm sunny France, where we wended our way slowly through the summer countryside to Paris, arriving there in the first week of September. Minnie's friend, Madame Nevada, met us at the station, and for two weeks we were overwhelmed by her hospitality. She took us to the theatre, to the circus, to the horse races at Auteuil and to the homes and estates of her friends. Finally, she seemed to run out of steam and we were left to our own devices.

In two more weeks we were due to cross the channel to England. It was then I should have introduced the thought that I would not be going with them. I had a ready-made excuse if I wanted one — I could say that I wanted to stay behind for a while and take instruction in my water-color technique. (I can't remember if I have mentioned that sketching and water colors had become a passion with me.) In any event I procrastinated until it was too late and before I knew it we were in residence at the Thames Hotel near Henley.

This was weak and foolish of me, because I knew that William would hear of our arrival; there had been too much publicity concerning our travels and about the composition of our party in the society columns for him to miss it. I wasn't sure whether or not he would get in touch, but I secretly hoped so. It was wicked of me to put him in such a dilemma.

Here I go digressing again into my own personal life when I'm supposed to be telling you about your mother and father. To put it briefly, I did see William — not once but several times. It was thrilling, yet each occasion was ruined. My emotions were so confused and my tongue so guarded that it was impossible to say anything that rang true. He, too, was stiff and altogether it was more frustrating than pleasurable, especially when compared to our easy camaraderie on previous occasions. He was even more handsome than ever — not that he looked any younger than his fifty years; age had just put the finishing touches on him.

After seeing him at several social occasions and knowing that we would inevitably meet again at others, I became nervous and realized that I wanted to leave England and get back to America.

I was not the only one. Your mother had maintained the greatest composure throughout the trip, but from the moment we set foot in England, she had been fidgety and almost irritable. In retrospect, I know that she was feeling the pull of our imminent departure and was beginning to anticipate seeing your father again. I found a poem that she inscribed in her scrapbook that she obviously thought expressed her feelings.

SLOW FATHER TIME

Why art so slow, oh Father Time?
When he and I are parted;
With him my days are all sunshine
While now I'm heavy-hearted
So quicken then thy pace for me,
Thy feet may feel no tether;
If thou need'st rest, permit I thee
To lag when we're together.

While we were in Europe, your father was struggling along in Cleveland with his apprenticeship at the gas company. In his letters to your mother, he had carried his reminiscences about their summer in York about as far as he could, and now he was running into difficulty finding subjects of interest to write about. He had re-appraised his situation and was becoming doubtful of the gas business as one suitable for his life work, but was still trying to convince himself as the following letter shows:

Then I received your letter saying you had heard nothing from me, that you were very wroth, that I had fallen from your good graces, that you didn't think I was much of a friend, that you were a better friend to me than I was to you, which is impossible, and so you can see, dear friend, I am much distressed. You may have written five times to my twice, and though, Lord knows, I was glad enough for everything I got, honestly now — only one of yours was a really truly nice long letter, and all of mine were just as long, which shows much good will, if only half as nice.

I can send you no pretty cards from Tivoli, for we print none such at the gas works, still, being hampered as I am by truth, I have done my very level best. I am so sorry you thought me forgetful, but I'm awfully glad that you had the faith to write and tell me, dear friend, that you still trusted me. I value that trust, and to think that it has been sorely tried by the straying of my letters is very annoying, for you know perfectly well that I had no other motive in writing than to give constant proof of my fidelity. I will write every minute, rather than you should think for a moment that I was a false friend after all.

My hilarious life of wild frivolity is just the same. I work along, ride horseback twice a week, and dine occasionally or marry somebody, that is to say, I go and rejoice at somebody's downfall, and then I work some more and wonder whether the weather will be any better soon, and if I'm going to have a cold, and take some quinine (do you remember?), and work some more, and ride some more, and eat again and sleep. It's a killing pace but I stand it.

I drew my salary last week. Think of it! It was gratifying to say, "I earned that myself," for the first time. With it, I shall build a steam yacht and pursue you, I think. All my friends are working out salaries or salvation somewhere else. Ethel has been sick with a trained nurse, Mother and Father are in Boston, and the crowd that I hunt with are all either East or in bed with nervous prostration, so these winter months are coolers all right.

I received a picture of our charming selves from Philadelphia last week. You are sitting against one of the piazza pillars on the railing of the Marshall House Hotel. I am standing beside you. Do you remember the day? It was the day we had our drive, I think, because my costume fails to suggest canoeing. Anyway, it was one day with you. That is sufficient.

And so we are now battering the hearts of Italian princes, oh my word, what a descent! You are off the home grounds. First we slaughter the scintillating Greenberg, then we harrow the sumptuous Kinnecutt, then the steward of the ship, and we have come down to princes, and Dago ones at that! . . .

Later he wrote:

. . . It is a funny world now, I tell you, and man is many-sided. Take this one for an example: Recall a day last summer, any day, when we two drifted on that river, and then sat under some green tree, reading Tennyson from time to time. Everything about shone with the glory of a summer day. The air was warm and fragrant, the grass and moss was soft and green, the sky above was blue with great white clouds drifting idly across it, and, as I lay at your feet, nothing broke the beauty of your voice, breathing the words of a great poet to me, and I was absolutely happy.

Yesterday I was told that the furnaces didn't work right, that an engineer had to come down from the makers and fix them, and that somebody (me), besides the superintendent, must be taught how to work them, so I was sent to see to it. I studied theories of combustion etc. . . . I was shown drawings, and then taken down into the cellar where everything was black. Dark forms drifted hither and thither in the smoke, I opened and shut doors and holes, and when I came out I felt all the exhilaration of something added.

Yet, in both cases, I am the same man, with the same brains, and instincts, and sensibilities. Why, then, can I feel pleasure in both extremes? Surely we are strange combinations, and it is fortunate that we are; we have only one life to live. I hope that mine may not be ever thus, as it runs now. Yet I am happy, I am interested and I am busy. It is rather a strange feeling I experience.

I often query thus. While attending, as I have, a university of "belles lettres," where what is best in poetry, in literature, in art, and in culture is held in highest esteem, one sees things outside the university through a gorgeously colored glass.

Then one comes out here where men's minds are bent in other curves. One sees the power of iron, of steel, of coal; one encounters the man who thinks only of what can be done with steam, or electricity, or gas. Here is man turning the

175

forces of nature into railways and bridges and power of all kinds. They give their lives to it, their brains, their energy, their all.

It takes all kinds of people to make a world, and one often wonders whether after all there is not something inspiring in applied mechanics, and whether the man who can twist an iron bar to do his will has not done something after all. From your sweet poem one would infer that you thought he had.

God bless you, so do I.
M.S.G., Jr.

Finally, the following letter in which he wrote:

At last have I something of interest to relate, for I have broken loose . . . Some weeks ago my good sister Ethel, having recovered from her long illness, betook herself to Washington to visit her friend Alice Hay, so it behooved me to escort her and I had double reason for I could also see a good friend of mine, that same Alice Hay. I stayed nearby and took my meals with them. The Secretary himself is most cordial, to be sure. With his magic name we penetrated the most hidden recesses of the White House . . .

One Sunday night we were sitting about when the Secretary asked me if I should like to go to the White House to a bit of a Sunday night musicale. Of course I leapt at the chance, so away we went.

The President was in the outer hall behind the glass doors, so that my introduction to him was simple, and quiet. He was most cordial and sent us in to his wife, who was in the Blue Parlor. The room is of an oval shape, done all in turquoise blue, and Mrs. McKinley sat with Mrs. Hobart at one end, while members of the cabinet, a few senators, and soldiers chatted along the walls.

When I appeared with the Secretary of State, there was an absolute silence in which I walked the length of the room, and was presented . . . Mark Hanna I knew and Mrs. Alger, so I got on comfortably enough, but that short walk almost ossified me. My Aunt! but I was frightened almost unto death.

Now I am here again; the rest of the family have all gone south and I am left alone, in all the rain and snow I ever hope to see, to hold the fort and work. I ride still, and work, and eat, and that's all. Everybody is south. There is absolutely nothing to do, but I am existing still. I shall be glad if, when Easter comes and the Lord is risen, the thermometer has also risen.

His next letter was most interesting.

. . . Monday I returned, stopping at Pittsburgh to see the company coal mine. I was met at the station by a private locomotive in which we flew out to the mine. Have you ever seen a coal mine? Well, you must imagine a little square hole in the side of a mountain about 1000 ft. up, with a little railroad track (like those used at roller coasters), running from this pit mouth to the foot of the hill, where the coal is loaded and shipped. Down this hill fly tiny cars in trains of five, out onto the "tipple" where they are weighed and emptied, and then back again into the mine to be refilled.

A mine is made up of a large main entry with chambers coming off on each side as in a hotel. Through this entry run the car tracks which branch into the chambers. The cars are drawn by mules that haul them all about under the ground to be filled by the miners. Each miner fills his car, puts a number into it, and then, when it gets outside it is weighed and put to his credit, for he is paid by the ton.

The miner removes the coal by first cutting out a triangle, just as a man cuts a notch into a tree. Then he drives a wedge in above his cut and the coal falls at his feet. Of course, it is very hard to make this cut as he lies on his side and cuts straight into the face of his chamber.

Having arrived at the mine, we donned rubber coats and ensconced ourselves in one of the empty coal cars, which shot us up the slope like a young rocket. At the top we were attached to a train of 73 cars, all also empty and going into the mine on a cable road. Away we went, crashing, turning, twisting, with a rattle and a roar which in the absolute pitchy blackness was appalling. Nothing could be seen but the shining, dripping roof of coal above us, lit by the flaming lamp on the front of the trainman's cap. We dashed up to a group of men. Small boys ran hither and thither; men joked and laughed as though they were not a mile underground, and away we went again. Here and there the light would show a miner huddled out of the way in a niche, or a mule crouching against the wall till the train went by.

Far underground we left the train, hitched a mule to a car, and went on and on. Huge openings — the chambers — began to show on the sides, and far, far back in one, a single light showed where a miner earned his daily bread. At last we alighted and entered one of those rooms. Huge lumps of coal, the day's work, lay waiting for the car, and the miner crouching low, swung his pick about him, cut far into the rock and pried until his coal came crashing down. Save for his tiny light, all about was absolute darkness — silent, cold, and damp.

Think of a life such as that. Yet from that dark silence comes all that makes the steamer go, the railroad carry you from place to place — the power, the light, the money, and the things that bring you comfort and pleasure. The man that makes it all possible lives by himself in absolute darkness, day after day, and earns $1.79 for each of those days. From that coal comes gas with all its light and heat, and ammonia with all its applications. It's a wonderful chain, dear friend, but I'm glad we flew out of that place as fast as we came in, and I'm glad I was born on the other end of the chain.

Quite a description of the nineteenth century miner, isn't it?

Chapter 17

Despite his avowals to the contrary your father was not happy to be in the gas business, especially the gas business in Cleveland, Ohio. He was far too much of an intellectual to be happy in any business career. He was also depressed by the thought that even when your mother returned from Europe he would still be unable to see her and, if he wasn't around, eventually someone else would take his place in her affections.

He came up with what I think was a brilliant plan — he decided to become a lawyer, a profession much more suited to his talents than the gas business. He applied to Harvard Law School and was accepted for admission in the fall of 189 . He had a tremendous fight with your grandfather about this sudden abandonment of the gas business, but with a lot of support from your grandmother, he finally got permission and the financing he needed.

At one stroke, he got himself back in his beloved "East," and into a profession more suited to him, with summers and other school vacations free to pursue his courtship of your mother.

When we got back to Philadelphia, there, on the front hall table, was a letter from him announcing this great change in his life. I saw your mother's face as she quickly read it. The sudden glow that came over her announced her pleasure as though she had spoken it out loud. Your father had been at his studies for a month by then, was doing well, and promised to come to Philadelphia soon.

He arrived at our door on a blustery Saturday afternoon in November with a barely plausible excuse for being in town. We were all in the living room on the second floor when he was shown up, and a more nervous young gentleman I have seldom seen — trying to be casual, trying not to devour your mother with his eyes, and at the same time attempting to address himself to Minnie and Charlie, but failing to hear their responses to his inanities. I never heard so many "I beg your pardons?" in my life — it was a shambles.

Finally, taking pity on him, Minnie invented an excuse to withdraw herself, Charlie, and me from the room, leaving your parents alone. It didn't take them long to get to the point, as I later learned, and all the feelings that they had hinted at in their letters were spoken aloud and in plain language. There was no formal proposal of marriage at that time, but there was a tacit understanding that if they could they would marry.

It was late afternoon when they went out for a walk to the park in Rittenhouse Square. Arm in arm, with the wind swirling the dead leaves around their feet, they walked off down the street. I was just returning from an errand when they walked right by me without seeing me at all, they were so wrapped up in each other. Seeing their happy faces, I did not break the spell.

The winter passed without any particular incident that I can recall. Your parents saw each other from time to time and wrote continually. There was always a letter to or from one of them on the front hall table. Your father was working very hard, and in March he had a serious intestinal attack that forced him to retire from all studies for three weeks. He recovered well, but it hurt his marks, of course, and he was very disappointed about that because, for once, he was trying to excel.

When I say that the winter passed without incident it was not quite so, because coming into the twentieth century was an incredible event in itself. No one knew what was to come, but there was such a feeling of expectancy of great things about to happen. So much had happened in the last decade of the nineteenth century that the advent of a new century seemed to ensure even further wonders.

That summer of 1900 we were all at Bar Harbor, Maine, staying at Rodick's Hotel, famed for its five hundred rooms, the longest and widest piazzas in the country, and its lobby, known as "the Fish Pond," where, as one society writer said, "Easy-going Philadelphia girls taught slow-going Boston boys how to flirt."

Mt. Desert Island had a very active summer life then. A lot of prominent people were there such as Endicott Peabody, your headmaster at Groton, Bishop Lawrence of Boston, the famous Fritz Kreisler, and many luminaries from the diplomatic corps. Your father and his family were staying at the Inn at Dark Harbor on Islesboro Island, about twenty miles away by steamer through the Eggemoggin Reach. He came over often to see your mother and to attend one of the many social events: a "Hop," a tally-ho party, or a canoe contest.

That was the summer they became secretly engaged. I know only that it happened one day when they had taken a picnic lunch out on a sailboat to a little deserted island, and that your father agreed that he would come to Philadelphia in the fall and ask your grandfather Whelen for permission to marry.

This he did, and although I was in New Orleans at the time, and your mother and father were sworn to secrecy for more than a year, I did hear all about it later.

Your father arrived in Philadelphia on a warm day in October 1900, took a hansom cab through the windy, leaf-strewn streets to the Rittenhouse Club, and once there sent a note to Mr. Whelen at his office saying that he had arrived and would await Mr. Whelen at the club at dinner time.

They had a pleasant meal, then retired to a quiet corner of the lounge for coffee, brandy and cigars. Taking a deep breath your father said, "Mr. Whelen, as you know, I am here to ask for permission to marry Violett." He went on for some time about his love for your mother and his prospects until finally Charlie interrupted him.

"Of course," Charlie said, "we have known all about it since Violett told us when she came back from Maine. Mrs. Whelen and I have had much conversation on the subject, and I won't pretend that it wasn't quite a shock when we heard the news. We knew that you and Violett were very fond of each other, but had no idea that matrimony was in the picture.

"Now we think you are a fine boy and could make Violett a good husband, but in view of your present position as a student at the law school, we feel that there should be no announcement of an engagement until you have graduated and secured a position with a firm."

And so it was to be. Your father went back to his studies in Cambridge, and your mother went on with her life, pretending to be as uncommitted as the next girl. They were both remarkably discreet. Even

I didn't know of their engagement until a month before the actual announcement.

The next summer (1901), they were able to see each other on a regular basis on Islesboro Island in Maine where both families were staying — the Greenough family renting a house overlooking the Tarratine Yacht Club, and we staying at the Inn at Dark Harbor.

The Inn at Dark Harbor was one of the loveliest of its kind, one of those turn-of-the-century summer hotels with high-ceilinged bedrooms and higher-ceilinged public rooms. It was enclosed on three sides by wide piazzas with dark green wooden floors, furnished with clusters of wicker furniture.

Built by a group of Philadelphia investors in the early 1890's, the Inn was situated on a promontory on the west side of Islesboro Island overlooking the waters between the island and the mainland, with the Camden hills in the distance. Just below the Inn to the south was Dark Harbor, so called because it is completely surrounded by tall pines that shadow the water except during the noon hours.

To call it a "harbor" is a slight exaggeration, since its whole area doesn't exceed a quarter mile in diameter, and the entrance is too shallow for all but the smallest boats. In the 1890's the Inn filled this entrance with large rocks, leaving a sluiceway so that the "harbor" was turned into a huge salt-water pool for the use of its guests. Below the Inn about one mile to the north was the ferry landing, where guests arrived from Rockland. There were few other accommodations for visitors on the island except for private homes, so the pace of life was rather slow.

For recreation, there was the Islesboro Golf Club and the Tarratine Yacht Club. Horses could be hired, and there were lawn tennis "areas" both at private homes and at the Inn. And of course there was a lot of walking along the shoreline, with its lovely views of sun-warmed, sea-weed-smelling rocks, ocean, islands, and sailboats, with never the angry buzz of a gasoline engine to break the peace.

At the Tarratine Yacht Club at Dark Harbor your father and grandfather raced their new boat "Bagheera" that season of 1901 and came in third for the summer series. In July, they came in second in the Sloan Cup race, beaten by Peter Kissel in a very close match.

When the boat wasn't wanted for racing, your mother and father took long, leisurely sails on the sun-lit waters around the island, anchoring for lunch in some small deserted cove or leaving the boat at a convenient dock and carrying their wicker picnic hamper to a high point where they could settle themselves in the shade of a pine and look out over the sea. Many an afternoon was spent this way with the smell of the ocean mixing in a light breeze with the scent of pine. They would eat and talk, read poetry to each other, and sometimes your mother would sing for your father.

In a more public way, they swam in the huge man-made pool of Dark Harbor, where the water was considerably warmer than the ocean. (That is to say, the men swam; the ladies "bathed," our clothing not permitting any extended distances in the water.) They played tennis, but only a little, because your father was not too fond of the game.

At night after dinner there was usually a small band in the dining room and they would dance. Your mother loved to dance, but not so much as your father, for whom it was a passion. He danced very well and enjoyed displaying his excellence. When the evening was over he would walk your mother back down the long, dimly lit corridor to Minnie's room. They would hold each other's hands, talk quietly for a while about their plans for the morrow, and say goodnight.

So it went on, day after day. It was another "glorious summer," almost as glorious as York Harbor in 1898. In late August, both the Greenoughs and the Whelens left Islesboro taking the side-wheeler steamboat from Rockland to Boston. The Greenoughs continued on by train to Cleveland, but the Whelens and your father, who was not due back in law school until later, had been invited by a Mr. Henry Clay Pierce, also at Islesboro, to spend a few days with him and his family at their seaside summer home on Paine Avenue in Prides Crossing, Massachusetts.

Mr. Pierce was a multi-millionaire from St. Louis, a crony of Frick, Carnegie, and a Paine Avenue neighbor, Judge William Moore, who had introduced Pierce to the delights of the North Shore, and Paine Avenue in particular. (Never a real judge, Moore made his greatest financial killing by buying the Rock Island Railroad on margin and named his palatial home on Paine Avenue "Rockmarge" in honor of his coup.) When the train let us off at the Prides Crossing station, Mr. Pierce's "station wagon" was there to meet us and bring us to his estate called "Harbor View," a six-acre, pie-shaped piece of land at the very end of the avenue, whose outer rim was on the water, with an entrance off Paine Avenue through the point of the "pie."

There were two houses and a stable on the property. The main house on the left was a huge whale of a building with white clapboards and a shingled roof with many dormers and undulating levels that followed the contours of the complicated plan for the rooms below. In front was a long pier and a float from which Mr. Pierce could board his steam yacht, usually to be seen moored several hundred yards offshore.

To the right of the entrance was the stable and beyond it a large, shingled guest house. Huge as the main house was it was not sufficient for the number of guests Mr. Pierce liked to entertain and hence this added facility.

We were there for five days. Your parents walked together on West Beach and joined the other guests on the steam yacht for trips to Marblehead to watch the races, and once we went for a whole day's trip to the Isle of Shoals and back. On the return trip, we dined aboard at a large table set up in the stern as the yacht steamed along over calm seas in the moonlight.

Too soon it was over, and we were on our way back to Philadelphia, and your father to Cambridge. It had been another lovely summer for your parents, but they were a long way from being formally engaged. Your father had one more year at law school and was having a hard time trying to balance his desire to excel with the limitations imposed by his then delicate health. Your mother, too, was having her difficulties fending off other suitors without insulting them on the one hand, or giving your father too much cause for jealousy on the other. This was hard to do when she couldn't tell them that she was promised to your father, but that was part of the agreement. Both of them were walking a tightrope, and I must say they did it well.

They were relieved that although permission for an official announcement was still withheld, Minnie was no longer attempting to "divert" your mother. She had taken your mother abroad, introduced her to a number of sterling prospects and given her a coming-out party after their return. She had done her best and she knew when to quit. As always, Minnie did so with a grace that left no bitter aftertaste to spoil things for anyone.

It is important for you to appreciate the tenacity of your mother and father in the face of such parental opposition. They were still living in an era when marriages, if not completely arranged, were carefully thought about by the parents, especially the daughter's parents, who still expected to exert a large degree of control over her betrothal. At this time marriages of American society beauties to European nobility were considered the ultimate social success, and social success was a very important thing to American parents of the so-called upper class. Many an American heiress was forced into a loveless marriage with a titled European aristocrat for the vanity of having a title in the family.

The shock to the Whelens was not that your father fell in love with your mother, or even that she found him so wonderfully attractive. The shock was that she loved him enough to defy her family and insist on the marriage. Indeed, Ma, perhaps the most passionate advocate of your mother marrying a title, did not give her full approval of your father until a few days before the actual marriage.

It was a long fall and winter for both your parents, but after a great deal of hard work and, fortunately, no further serious illness, your father passed his final exams, and in June 1902 he received his LLB degree from Harvard. Your mother, her brother Charlie, Minnie and I stopped over in Boston to attend his Commencement Day exercises on our way from Philadelphia to Islesboro, Maine.

The Whelens stayed at the Hotel Vendôme on Commonwealth Avenue — at that time the newest and most luxurious hotel in Boston. Your father's family all came back from Cleveland for the great event and your grandfather took the whole group to dinner at the Somerset Club the night before Commencement Day.

It was a hot, humid night and the ladies' dining room on the first floor was particularly airless, but your mother and father gave it little thought. Their families had finally agreed that they could marry, and a formal announcement was to be made later that summer. Toasts were made to the happy couple and by the happy couple, and the evening was a great success. Now that the marriage was an accepted fact, everyone relaxed and enjoyed each other immensely. No one could imagine why there had ever been any doubt about it. Minnie was her usual charming self, and your grandfather was positively gallant. Your aunt Eugenia, who was just sixteen, sat in speechless wonder throughout the evening.

After dinner, your father got Minnie's permission to walk your mother back to her hotel; Minnie, Charlie Jr., Eugenia and I would take a carriage. It was cool and quiet as the young couple strolled slowly under the sighing trees by the duck pond in the Public Garden. Passing down Arlington Street in our carriage, I saw that they had stopped for a while on the bridge to look back over the water to the winking gas streetlights on Beacon Street.

It was hot again the next day, and Harvard Yard was dry and dusty, crammed with graduates in their caps and gowns, and their families all in their finest dress. Your father, in traditional law school cap-and-gown, escorted us to our seats next to his family, then went off to sit with his classmates. It was a most enjoyable occasion for this determined couple — a moment of pride and triumph for them both, as your father received his professional credentials in the presence of his family, his betrothed and her family.

After the ceremony we all walked down to the Charles River, where the Greenoughs had arranged for a picnic to be set up under a tree by the water's edge. We were close to the boat house, and every so often a muscular, mustached young man in that quaint, stripe-shirted costume they wear for rowing would appear on the float carrying an elegant shell over his head, which he would then place gently in the water and row off with soft, chunking noises.

Behind us were the red brick buildings of Harvard with an occasional white spire piercing the blue sky. Along the bank were many other family groups like ours, while overhead bosomy white clouds lazed along. Looking back at it in my mind the scene is as clear as a painting on the wall, but better than a painting because I can so vividly recall the feel of the drowsy heat, the murmurous sounds, and the dusty smells of that day, and I can still see your parents, standing apart by the river's edge, talking quietly.

Chapter 18

The announcement of the engagement was made on July 12, 1902, from Islesboro, Maine, and what a splash it made in the social pond. Your parents and everyone else in the family who knew ahead of time had kept the secret so well that the engagement was a real surprise to everyone and quite a shock to some, such as suitors like Huidekoper, Pier, Otis, and especially Haywood Shreve of Philadelphia, who thought himself almost irresistible. He had proposed to your mother and she had refused him, but he planned to ask her again and predicted that she would accept. To say that he was shocked by the announcement would be an understatement.

Newspaper accounts and letters of congratulation came pouring in. One paper referred to your mother's "stunning manner of carrying herself that is to be seen among the best families of the North, yet tempered with the grace found in well-bred Southerners." Other articles called her "THE belle of Philadelphia, . . . one of the most beautiful and talented young women in fashionable life . . ." ". . . she has a real charm of manner that gives her a distinction all her own." We were so proud of her.

Your father gave your mother a simple diamond solitaire engagement ring and a small book containing a single poem called "Marpessa," by Stephen Phillips. The book is inscribed "To my darling, blessed girl, in memory of all the times this wonderful poem has gained its beauty for me in coming from your lips, and with the promise to do my best, in the glory of your love, to give to you but my tiny portion of what you bring to me."

The book has little marginal notes made by your father, as he said, "not in the hope of adding to the poem, . . . but as the wind coming over the sea raises little waves to kiss the very breeze that gives them life, so will my comments show where the words touched my soul."

The poem tells the story of the wooing of a girl called Marpessa by a mortal named Idas and the god Apollo. In the end she choose Idas, telling Apollo

> . . . but if I live with Idas, then we two
> On the low earth shall prosper hand in hand
> In odours of the open field, and live
> In peaceful noises of the farm, and watch
> The pastoral fields burned by the setting sun.
>
> And he shall give me passionate children, not
> Some radiant god that will despise me quite,
> But clambering limbs and little hearts that err.
> And I shall sleep beside him in the night,
> And fearful from some dream shall touch his hand,
> Secure.

I think that little quote expresses a lot of your parents' feelings for each other and the kind of life they intended to lead. Someday you must read the whole poem. It's dated in style, of course, but I know, somehow, that it will affect you as it does me.

Your mother put all the letters of congratulation in a scrapbook and I have just reread them to refresh my memory. Here are some samples:

In her letter, your aunt Eugenia said she "gave a 'warhoop' of joy right on Commonwealth Avenue" when she heard the news, and "Ma said I would certainly be arrested."

Your great uncle Ned Violett wrote Violett hoping "that your new life will be one continual stream of Elysian bliss" and called her "a perfect woman, nobly planned."

Ma's letter expressed her feelings quite succinctly:

> Your very sweet letter announcing your engagement did
> not surprise me in the least as I was confident Mallie was the

favored one notwithstanding all your flirtations with other devoted lovers. I am glad to know that you will realize all the happiness you wish for in uniting your fate with his.

You say he possesses all the qualities of mind, heart and disposition to insure a happy union. I of course have been very ambitious for you to make a brilliant marriage, possessing as you do so many attractions to make you a Shining Star in the social world, but your happiness must be our first consideration and I hope you have chosen wisely.

His love and devotion to you for many years shows his loyalty and steadfastness of character and certainly he deserves some reward, but what a prize he has won for this fidelity . . .

. . . I do so hate to give you up my darling — it seems so hard to realize you are about to cross the threshold to wifehood. It seems so short a time ago when you were nestling in my arms at the dear old farm, just the sweetest darling that ever was except my own, begging me so hard, "Grandma do tell me another story." . . .

Yours fondly —
Grandma Violett

Suitors wrote to complain of their bad luck and to make such comments as ". . . to think that the proud Miss Whelen should be willing to promise to obey anyone . . . ," ". . . I am going right down to Schellenberger's for a dark crepe suit, and I shall never look cheerful again," ". . . to think of Mally's luck! I really can't get over it — Incidentally, I suppose you are to be congratulated yourself for getting such a fine fellow . . . "

Reginald Huidekoper was particularly hard hit by the news. He had had some very serious thoughts about your mother himself and no inkling that she was involved with anyone else. He wrote in part:

No one could know you half as well as I — and I used to think we knew each other pretty well — without feeling that a jewel of such a quality as you is the rarest thing in the world . . .

Though I never told you what I thought of you, and of course cannot do so now, I can say that any man on whom you should bestow such an honor and such a compliment, ought to get down on his knees and thank God for the day he was born and the lucky day he met such a woman . . .

. . . I have seen a great many in my little life, but have had but one ideal since I went to Oxford, and I am frank to say, had my little sister lived, I should rather have had her like Violett Whelen than anyone else that I have had the good fortune to meet . . .

. . . Dear Violett, I cannot tell you how much I wish you all the happiness in the world. I know it is a case of true love, I could tell that at Prides Crossing a year ago, and in this age and generation I congratulate you on choosing such a man with such refined tastes and clean life as Mally. Men nowadays are by no means all they should be, but I know Mally pretty well, and I should have to do some lying to tell anything about him which would cause anyone to hang their head.

I wish you a long and happy life and as the poet says:
"As a wave follows a bark o'er the sea,
E'en so may happiness e'er follow thee."

It took him fifteen years to get over your mother. I remember reading the announcement of his marriage to Bessie du Pont of Wilmington, Delaware, in 1917.

Your mother's girl friends wrote such things as ". . . after I read your letter I hurdled every chair in the room, upset a table and landed finally in a heap on the windowsill," or "Oh the thrill of it — the wonder of it and the blessed happiness of it all! . . . MRS. Greenough! I can't believe my eyes! . . . I am bursting . . ."

Your great uncle Barrett Wendell described your mother in his letter to your father saying, "She has that kind of marvelous instinct, which comes to really good women and none other . . ." About your father, he said, "You are one of the few for whom my affection is strengthened by a kind of admiration, and a rapport of spirit, which you are hardly yet of an age to understand." He went on, "You and she have truly more to give one another than most human beings found in this puzzling world."

There are many letters to your father in the scrapbook, all filled with complimentary remarks and interesting asides. You should read them all, but it would be too cumbersome to quote very much from them here. Here are just a few examples:

Your father's cousin Frazier Curtis wrote from New York, where he was working for John Jacob Astor:

Dear Green —

Your letter calls up vague memories of an Italian gentleman who once remarked "How long, O Cataline!" ... I want to congratulate you very heartily on your success in the great plunge. I thought Miss Whelen a very sweet girl indeed and believe and trust that with her you will always be as happy as you are now. It does seem like a pretty good start in this silly old world to have someone like that to care for you and for you to work for . . .

What with you and Riggs and Johnson gone, not to mention Piggerson, the old place is beginning to look rather bare. However, with the support of Jackson I expect to hold the fort this many a long year. If it isn't asking too much you might kiss Miss Whelen for me, and at any rate give her my best wishes.

I want to see you as soon as possible for a handshake and a really good chin over the whole business.

Yours —
Slim

Also from New York City was the following:

Dear, dear old Greenberg,

I'd like to wait until I get home tonight away from the steam drills and typewriters and then sit down and try to say some of the things that never can be said. But I can't wait any longer. Your letter from Dark Harbor came to me last night. It was the greatest and happiest kind of a surprise . . .

I am so glad, Mally, so deeply and truly and proudly happy for you, that it seems almost a sacrilege for me to attempt to put any of it into words. It seems to me that the futures of men like you and Riggs, and a few others, make up for all the cheap, materialistic and characterless fizzles that form the background of human experience . . .

I am proud of you, Greenberg, with all my heart — proud of the courage and fidelity with which you have stuck to ideals not easy to live up to; and more proud than I can tell you of the sacred reward that you now have for those qualities . . . I had the honor of meeting Miss Whelen once several years ago. I only saw her for a minute or two, and it is hardly possible that she remembers it, but I have never forgotten . . .

> Ever your loving friend
> *N.P.*

N.P. was Norton Perkins, a Harvard classmate of Malcolm's and a fellow Law School graduate.

Finally a light and delightful little note from his Harvard classmate Charlie Jackson:

. . . as I have never met Miss Whelen I shall refrain from extolling her house-wifely characteristics, her clean floors, her flakey pie crusts, her neat darns and her exquisite laundry work. I have never even seen her full face so I can't sing its praises, but fortunately I have seen her profile and it was one of the handsomest I ever had the pleasure of looking on. Good luck to you, old boy.

I should like to write Miss Whelen and tell her what a hero you are, but as I have no idea where she is I am afraid I shall have to forego the pleasure . . . It is very hot here and I think I shall have to adjourn to the BAA [Boston Athletic Association] and drink a Thomas Collins to your Health —

> *C. Jackson*

P.S. In reading your note a second time I see that Miss

The Violetts

Left: Sixteen-year-old Lily Violett in 1870. Below left: William Alfred Violett ("Papa") in 1862. Below right: Penelope Oldham Violett ("Ma") in 1907; she was eighty-two.

*L*eft: Lily Violett (left) and little brother Ned in 1859. Below left: Heliotrope (Ella) Violett at nineteen, when but for the War, she would have been well launched as a "Belle."

*A*bove right: Ella, debutante manquée, in her mid-twenties. Right: Atwood Violett in his early thirties, a successful businessman.

*B*elow: *This photograph was taken while the Violetts (except Atwood) were vacationing in Bryn Mawr, Pennsylvania, in the summer of 1877. From bottom left, clockwise: Ella (aged 27); Lily (aged 23); unknown; Ma (aged 52); Mignonette (aged 20); and Ned (aged 21). Shown in close-up are: Lily, Ma, Ella, and Minnie.*

The Whelens

As photographed in 1878, left: Charles Smith Whelen, and below: Mignonette Violett Whelen in her wedding dress.

*B*elow: Six-month-old
*Violett Whelen, June,
1881. Right: Minnie
holding her newly
christened daughter Violett,
April, 1881.*

*A*bove: Charles Smith
*Whelen, Jr. at age two in
1886. Right: A year later
with his sister Violett.*

Penelope Violett (Ma) was visiting the Whelens at "Nestledown" in 1888 when the pictures on this page were taken. Note little Charlie's long curls and Lord Fauntleroy clothes.

*I*n 1895, Violett *(right) was
fifteen, and Minnie (below), a
fashionable Philadelphia matron
of thirty-eight.*

*T*op left: *Violett pouring tea in her room at Dana Hall School in 1897. Top right: "Young Charlie" Whelen in 1903.*
Abroad in 1898 — above: Violett helping Cousin Elsie to drink from a well bucket. Right: Setting out for a drive from their hotel in Italy are (left to right) coachman, Violett, Huidekoper, Aunt Laura, Minnie, coachman, and Cousin Elsie.

Above: Reginald S. Huidekoper. Right: Violett (with parasol) and friends at the summit of Mt. Pilatus.

The Greenoughs

Malcolm Scollay Greenough and his wife Lizzie Tiffany Greenough as photographed in 1875 (below) and in 1889 (bottom).

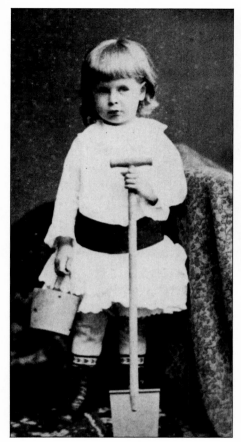

*A*bove: *Malcolm Scollay Greenough, Jr., 1879; Top right: M.S.G., Jr. and father in 1881. Center right: Eugenia and Ethel Greenough in 1895. Bottom right: The Greenough children in 1890. Left to right are Ethel (standing), Eugenia, Charles, and M.S.G., Jr.*

*Photographed in 1902 —
right: Malcolm with gloves
and walking stick. Below:
Violett wearing a "boa."
Opposite page: Violett in her
wedding dress, April,
1903.*

Right: Violett and Malcolm on their honeymoon, 1903. Below: Some of the 463 wedding presents received.

Left: 1904 — *a grief-stricken Minnie holding her baby grandson, Malcolm Whelen Greenough. Below: 1906 — "Mally" sitting on Grandmother Minnie's knee.*

Right: 1911 — *Lily and her great nephew Mally photographed at Atlantic City. Bottom right: Malcolm Whelen Greenough in 1925. Bottom left: Last known photograph of Aunt Lily — the Adirondacks, 1933.*

Whelen is staying with you. Tell her yourself what a hero you are and say if you choose that them's my sentiments.

Your parents spent the rest of the summer in a whirl of parties. What little time they had to themselves they devoted to their favorite pastimes of sailing and picnicking. They were so happy they seemed to glow, and their pleasure was so infectious that we were all raised to a level of enjoyment that seemed too good to be true.

In September we returned to Philadelphia, where I stayed for only a few weeks before returning to New Orleans to help take care of Ma, who had become quite ill. Your father went on to Cleveland to start the practice of law. During the fall your mother made several visits there, and occasionally your father visited her in Philadelphia.

In late November I got a telegram from Minnie asking me to come to Philadelphia because your father had become extremely ill with what they feared was appendicitis. She and your mother had gone to Cleveland, and she wanted me to come and look after things while they were gone. By that time Ma was competely recovered, so I left immediately.

Appendicitis was diagnosed, and several weeks went by during which your father was kept in one position with ice packs around his abdomen to reduce the inflammation. Gradually his pain and fever subsided, but the doctors were convinced that, with his history of two prior attacks of this sort, it was too dangerous not to operate to remove the appendix. If it burst, your father would die.

They operated and successfully removed the highly inflamed appendix. Apparently there were no complications. Minnie came back to Philadelphia, but your mother stayed on and spent Christmas with the Greenoughs. Shortly after New Year's your father was recovered enough to return to work. Everything was back on track, and your mother went home to prepare for the April wedding.

I stayed on in Philadelphia for the rest of the winter to help with the wedding preparations. I won't go into all the details of that because it would be much too long and of no real interest except to those of us that went through it. By the first of April we were worn to a frazzle, and Charlie Senior had taken to spending much time at his club, but we had everything in hand.

I found a letter that your mother wrote your father shortly before their wedding, on the evening of April 6, 1903. After a hectic day, she was in her bedroom on the fourth floor, resting up before dinner. The guest bedroom on the third floor was filled to overflowing with wedding presents and there had been a steady coming and going of friends, relations and tradespeople all day long. In this quiet moment of the fading day, she sat at her desk by her window, high above Walnut Street where the trees below were budding misty green in the warm spring evening and wrote to her husband-to-be.

My darling loved one,

Oh! as the days come so near for you to come I can't tell you how I feel, a very agony of impatience and longing and a rhapsody of happiness and joy. Ah! you darling, I love you so, I love you so, and so many people seem to love you too. I never saw a man with so many men friends — every kind of friend. There are so many, many presents. You must have mentioned the fact that we had no carvers as we now have five sets. Isn't it funny!

Angel, will you forgive this hurried, horrid letter and know I am loving you in my heart so much, but I have been busy all day. I haven't had time to dress and it is now six-thirty and I am still in a dressing sash. People like Ruth Greenough, Mrs. Townsend, and your cousin Elsie are just back and other people like that, to whom I have to be polite and show them the presents myself, but I don't care who comes now except for Ethel and Esther Harrison, I won't show a single present until you come. Aunt Lily is here now, so she can show them, and Brother comes soon. We have nearly 300 presents and a week to go. Laura Biddle was supposed to have a great many and she had 340. I guess we will have about 350.

Dearheart, I am writing this postscript instead of resting because I really must tell you what happiness your blessed, darling letter brought to me this morning. Ah! beloved come to me soon that I may tell you in kisses and soft tender love words how I love you and how your love is the center, the joy, the great gladness of all my life, and your Sunday letter brought me such a deep happiness that no words can tell it, only you know what it means when I say darling I love you . . . always.

Dearheart — This is another little postscript for details.

I think you better write to all your ushers except Brother and tell them the engagements they have. That Laura Biddle expects them to lunch at "Wayne" on Sunday (12:45 train from Broad St.), and that Marion Curtis has Mr. Brookes (or Jackson, whichever you think best), Mr. Marvin, Mr. Dalton, and Mr. Kinnecutt to dine at 7:30 Sunday night. All details attended to now save a rush at the end, and you have no idea of the excitement here.

The wedding festivities started, as your mother wrote, on the weekend preceding the Tuesday service. Your father's family, the ushers and the out-of-town bridesmaids settled into their accommodations on Saturday, and that night his ushers gave him a quiet dinner at the Rittenhouse Club. On a warm, sunny Sunday the 12th of April, newly married Laura Whelen Biddle and her husband gave a large luncheon for the wedding party at their country estate at Wayne. At four-thirty Monday afternoon, there was the rehearsal at the church and later that evening the pre-wedding dinner party.

The weather, which had been so pleasant over the weekend, became cloudy and overcast on Monday afternoon, and by early Tuesday morning it was raining heavily.

The wedding was scheduled for noon, so we rose early, had a quick breakfast and went about our appointed tasks. Minnie gave final instructions to the cook and to the assembled servants, then left to check the floral decorations at the church. By nine-thirty she had returned and the bridesmaids started to arrive. With Ella in charge, they took over your grandmother's room and within moments it was awash with the enormous volume of their clothing.

Your mother, meanwhile, was in her room with Minnie, me, a maid and the dressmaker, going through the hours-long procedure of bathing, powdering, scenting, dressing, hairdressing, fixing, fastening, fussing and patting that was necessary to get everything just right for the great moment.

Downstairs on the second floor, the living room and the dining room were thrown into one by opening wide the doors of each room onto the hallway between them. Most of the furnishings were removed, and the whole floor was transformed for the reception to be held there after the wedding. Garlands of flowers were strung around the walls and placed on stands. Serving tables were set at strategic points, covered with white table linen that smelled of recent ironing, and the silver shone from careful polishing. Gleaming candelabras were set out, and in the kitchen a forest of champagne bottles were chilling in large tubs of ice. In the hallway, a small orchestra set up their stand and music holders and made practicing noises.

On the first floor, the reception room had been cleared of furniture, coat racks installed, and two maids assigned to relieve the guests of their damp clothing and help ladies repair any damages from the inclement weather.

The kitchen was a beehive of activity, where the cook and her extra helpers had been toiling since four in the morning to produce the food required. Just to be on the safe side, the wedding cake had been brought over from the baker's the night before and locked in the butler's pantry to prevent any accident.

Outside in the rain a line of closed carriages awaited the wedding party in the street by the front door, over which a green and white canopy had been erected. Aside from the occasional toss of a horse's head to shake off the rain, the line of carriages remained immobile, in strong contrast to the activity within.

Your father breakfasted with his family at the Aldine Hotel, then joined his ushers at the Rittenhouse Club, where your grandfather Whelen had engaged a suite of rooms for them to breakfast, dress in, and pass the morning. At about eleven-fifteen they all took a carriage to the church, the ushers remaining in the vestibule to seat the arriving guests, while your father and Frazier Curtis walked through to the rectory behind the chancel. There they waited, listening to the organ preludes and the growing murmur of the wedding guests as the church filled.

This was the Whelen family's church, the Holy Trinity Protestant Episcopal Church of Philadelphia, a large sandstone structure on the corner of Walnut Street and Rittenhouse Square, just two blocks from the Whelen house. Its interior dimensions were beautifully proportioned, with a high, barreled ceiling and large galleries on either side with tall stained glass windows behind them. The whole interior of the church is (I use the present tense because the church is still there — have you seen it?) a blend of warm, rich colors and materials. The floor is a terra cotta tile; the pews, columns and doors of polished dark mahogany; and the walls between the stained glass windows and murals a warm beige, adding lightness yet picking up the tints of the surrounding darker colors. Against this background, the gold columns and decorations around and on the altar shine like fire, making it an irresistible focal point in the church.

Elsie Whelen was, as promised, your mother's maid of honor. The bridesmaids were Marion Curtis (Frazier's sister and your father's cousin), your aunt Ethel, Josephine McIlvane, Adelaide Jordan, Edith Poor, and Sybil Kane. Then there was Bertha Lippincott, one of your mother's closest friends, and Esther White Harrison, standing in for her sister-in-law Marie Lemoine Harrison, your mother's other best friend, who unfortunately was too ill to attend.

Besides his best man, Frazier Curtis, your father's ushers were Charles Whelen, Jr., and Harvard classmates Philip Dalton, Hermann Kinnecutt, Langdon P. Marvin, Edward Thurston, Frederick Jordan and T. Mitchell Hastings.

Minnie was seated promptly at twelve noon, the organ switched to the traditional wedding march, your mother came down the aisle on Charlie's arm and there, waiting for her at the altar was your father.

As they stood before the altar and made their vows to each other, it was their supreme moment. It was just short of five years since they had first met and fallen in love. They had conquered all their difficulties and their love had grown, not withered, under the stress of separation and opposition. Now they were united by God, and no man could put them asunder. The road ahead was clear and only the most delightful prospects lay before them.

As the service concluded, your father kissed your mother, a slow sweet kiss, and then they turned, the organ pealed out the old familiar music, and they floated down the long central aisle packed on either side with their friends and relations, smiling happily and misty eyed at each other and the congregation. It was hard for them to believe that it was finally done; they were man and wife.

A newspaper account described the wedding well:

Few fashionable weddings in recent years have outshone this one which was witnessed by a large company. Wealth and fashion were represented in the assemblage which filled the Holy Trinity Church at noon yesterday. Despite the downpour of rain the church was crowded long before the ceremony began. The decorations were elaborate and beautiful. The chancel was banked with palms and Easter lilies. Over the railings were three arches covered with ferns and lilies. Bell-shaped floral ornaments were suspended from these arches with broad satin ribbons. As the familiar wedding march was heard, the bridesmaids advanced from the altar where they had been waiting and marched down the centre aisle to the back of the church where they were joined by the rest of the bridal party and the march to the altar was begun. Miss Whelen entered on the arm of her father and advanced to the chancel, where she was met by Mr. Greenough.

Miss Whelen wore an Empire gown of white satin, *en train,* embroidered with a design of white violets and green leaves. The bodice was trimmed with lace in bolero effect, the points hanging down long in front. Her long tulle veil was fastened with a wreath of orange blossoms and she carried a bunch of bride roses.

The maid of honor was gowned in violet crêpe de chine, with accordion-pleated skirt. A knotted sash was fastened in the middle of the back of the bodice, the long ends falling to the edge of the skirt. Her hat was of violet tulle trimmed with violets, and she carried a violet chiffon parasol ornamented with bunches of the same flowers. The bridesmaids' gowns were similarly constructed, but were of a pale blue shade. Their hats were of pale blue trimmed with violets, and their violet-decked parasols were of pale blue. Violet scarf pins were worn by the ushers, being the gift of the bridegroom. As the Reverend Mr. Tompkins performed the ceremony the organist played "Violets."

After the service there was a sumptuous "breakfast" at 2017 Walnut Street, which was as luxuriously decorated as the church, the prevailing flowers being lilies and violets. The champagne flowed and "everyone" was there — all the Philadelphia "names": the Biddles, the Harrisons, the Lippincotts, etc. A horseshoe-shaped table had been set up around three sides of the dining room, with your father and your mother at its center in front of the fireplace, the mantel shelf behind their heads covered with a mass of lilies and violets, and similar bouquets spaced out on the table.

Champagne was poured, toasts were made, the breakfast was consumed among the hustle and bustle of the servants and the extra staff hired for the occasion. Then all the tables were swiftly cleared and removed except the central one, and, with great ceremony, the butler and his assistant wheeled in the wedding cake, a large three-tiered cake topped with a beautifully crafted, pillared temple of marzipan. Under its little dome, behind the pillars and the bells hanging from ropes of flowers, were representations of the bride and groom. Family and guests gathered round in a circle and the servants clustered in the doorway to the kitchen area, all with champagne glasses in hand, watching with smiling pride as your mother and your father cut their wedding cake.

The band came on with a festive tune as they shared the first slice. Then the fathers of the bride and groom each proposed a toast, all drank, and the formal proceedings were over. Your mother's girl friends embraced her, and the men shook your father's hand and clasped his shoulder with smiling affection. Your parents went to speak to Ma, who gave them her official blessing from her seat in a corner of the room with all the regality that French blood and Southern gentility could command. (Ma could be quite an actress herself when she wanted to be.) Other elderly relatives were similarly visited before your father led your mother to the center of the drawing room.

They paused a moment, looking around the room with pleasure, then your father turned to your mother and held out his arms. She came into them exactly as she had that first night they met at York Harbor, the band struck up a waltz, and off they went, twirling and gliding a turn around the room and then another before your grandfather Greenough cut in and your father drew Minnie onto the floor. Charlie danced with your mother and then with your grandmother Greenough, and then the dancing became general. By old family custom, whenever your father danced with your mother, it was in the center of the room, where the other guests were careful to leave a small open space for them.

Your parents had decided to take a very short honeymoon after the wedding and a longer, more leisurely one later. First they went to the Whelen farm, Nestledown, at Morestein, Pennsylvania, near Bryn Mawr, for a few days of complete privacy and relaxation. The weather cleared and it was warm and peaceful there. The trees were just coming into bloom and were lightly clothed in hazy green. The days were sunny, with soft breezes carrying the wet spring wood smell to them as they walked together beside the pond and down to a little white cottage with a picket fence that stood beside the brook that fed the nearby pond. Beside the cottage was a small vegetable garden, its freshly turned earth pungent in the noonday sun. They sat on a nearby bench under a large shady oak and looked out over the pond's sun-dappled water, feeling utterly at peace with the world.

At night they ate in the long dining room overlooking the meadow and pond. The Whelens had two old servants, a man and his wife, who lived on the farm, and they took good care of their Miss Violett and her new husband.

A week later they took the train to New York City. They stayed at the Plaza Hotel, where your grandfather Greenough had provided them with a small suite on the fifth floor overlooking Central Park. This is the "old" Plaza Hotel now, built in 1896, but in 1903 it was one of the newest and most luxurious hotels in a city of luxurious establishments.

They went to the opera and heard the great Caruso in "Il Pagliacci." They spent a few evenings at the theatre and saw Strindberg's historical play, "Queen Christina," which they found rather dull, and on another night, J.M. Barrie's "Quality Street," which was much more appealing. An exciting novelty experience was their viewing of the new moving picture "The Great Train Robbery," the longest film to date — I think it lasted all of twelve minutes.

But, as your mother told me later, more precious to them than all their other activities were the long, quiet dinners together in some fine restaurant or more often, as they preferred, alone in their suite at the hotel. There they would have a table set in the bay window of the living room overlooking the park, lit here and there with gaslights and the moving pinpricks of carriage lamps. They would eat, drink their wine, and talk on and on until the guttering candles on the table moved them away to bed.

I can't tell you, Mally, how happy I was at your parents' wedding. I could hardly have been happier if it had been my own. Of course I did have a moment of sadness thinking of William and wishing that he were with me and that we were married ourselves and had come to see little Violett marry the handsome Yankee from Boston, but those thoughts only came to me once, when I was alone on the edge of the dancing. For the rest of the time, I was too busy and too engaged with what was going on to be anything else but happy in the reflected radiance of your parents' joy. Fortunately we cannot foresee the future.

Malcolm W. Greenough
89 Marlborough Street
Boston, Mass.

February 2, 1926

Dear Aunt Lily,

How can I tell you how much your last bit of writing affected me. For the first time in my life I feel as though I really know my mother and father. Up to now they have been like a dream that you can't quite remember when you wake up.

I've been to Islesboro, you know. Grandpa and I went there once when I was fifteen and he wanted to take a look at the old "Bagheera" before he sold her to Mr. Kissel. She was in pretty bad shape, but you could see what fine lines she had and imagine her as she used to be with her paint all fresh and her brightwork newly varnished. I suppose that's why Mr. Kissel wanted her. They said she was the last of her class around.

I remember we went down to look at Dark Harbor while we were on the island. The Inn is gone and the property is all overgrown, but you know, you can still see that old diving board way out by the blocked up entrance that they used when the guests from the Inn swam there.

I was in York Harbor once, too, cruising with Chan Bigelow and his parents. I'm not sure if it was the same Marshall House Hotel because there was some talk of a fire, but it looked just as you described it.

What a thrill it is for me to think that I have been to these places and walked where mother and father walked and seen the same things they saw. It makes a link with them that I never had before. Thank you so much for giving it to me.

I know the next part you write is going to be pretty sad, but again I only have the haziest idea of what really happened. It will be much better to know it all.

Thanks again from the bottom of my heart, dearest Aunt Lily; if you hadn't taken the trouble to do the work, all this would have been lost forever — not only to me, but to my children and grandchildren.

Your most affectionate nephew,
Mally

Chapter 19

Well, Mally, now we come to the part I have been dreading, but there's no way to avoid it, so here goes.

As I said in the last chapter, it was a short honeymoon and on May 1, 1903, they were in Cleveland where your father was to practice law in the firm of M.B. & H.H. Johnson. They moved into your grandparents' house at 724 Euclid Avenue while they looked for a house of their own. Their numerous wedding presents remained in Philadelphia until such time as there was a place to put them. It was warm, sunny May weather and Cleveland was looking its best.

The day after their arrival, your father went to work and your mother went house hunting with her new mother-in-law. They were almost immediately successful and found a very small brownstone town house about six blocks away from the senior Greenoughs. It was off the beaten path, on a small, tree-shaded side street that led to a little park. There was a cast iron fence in front of the house enclosing a small bit of grass and a short cement path to the front door. The house was two and a half stories high, not counting the basement, with a parlor, dining room and kitchen on the first floor and two bedrooms and a bath on the second. Like its neighbors, it had a fenced-in yard in back about eighteen feet square with a gate in back opening onto an alley. It seemed very "Bostonian" to your father, which meant he liked it a lot.

Your mother started shopping for furniture, rugs, draperies and all the other things she needed to start her household. Your father's pay was a bit better than they had anticipated and the rental on the house very reasonable, so it even looked as though they could afford one servant.

Two weeks later, your father woke up on Saturday morning with a bad cold and took to his bed. He was uncomfortable but cheerful. He spent Sunday in bed, too, with all the usual symptoms of a chest cold, including a heavy cough. Your mother brought him little bowls of soup and other dainties to tempt his appetite, smoothed his pillows, read to him, and did whatever else she could think of to make him comfortable. He said that if he weren't feeling so wretchedly, he would be enjoying himself, getting so much attention. Then the next day, your father had just finished a light lunch when suddenly, at about one P.M., he went into violent convulsions. There was nothing anyone could do and after a very short time he died, probably of heart failure brought on by the exertion and strain.

The family doctor had been called at once and came immediately, but it was too late. Your father was gone before he arrived, and there was nothing he could have done in any event. The only explanation that the doctors could come up with was that a blood clot caused by his operation in December had slowly traveled through his body to his brain and caused the convulsions.

Your mother, hysterical with grief and shock, was given a strong sedative and put to bed. Your grandmother Greenough was stunned; she did not cry, nor say a word. She simply went into the parlor where she sat in the corner of the sofa with her hands folded in her lap, her shoulders hunched over, and stared at the floor until long after sunset. Your grandfather looked in on her but decided it was best to leave her as she was, so he walked down to the telegraph office and confirmed the awful fact by sending a wire to the other Greenoughs and the Whelens in Philadelphia informing them that his son was dead.

The Greenough family, with your mother and Minnie, who had come on immediately from Philadelphia, made the long, sorrowful train trip with your father's body back to Boston the next day. Minnie told me that your mother wanted to sit in the baggage car with your father's body, but the conductor wouldn't let her. She was over her tears though, and sat in the compartment looking out the window at the passing scenery during the whole of the trip. Finally the train pulled into the Back Bay Station in Boston, and the long, agonizing journey was over.

The funeral was held in the chapel at the Mt. Auburn Cemetery in Cambridge, Massachusetts, at three o'clock on May 20, 1903. The weather was unusually warm and summer-like and the little chapel was crowded. The Whelens and the Greenoughs were all there, of course, and, poignantly, the pall bearers were for the most part your father's ushers of a month past. Frazier Curtis, Frederick Jordan, Mitch Hastings, Langdon Marvin, Hermann Kinnecutt, Phil Dalton, Charlie Jackson, Henry Brooks, and Cliff Payson made up the sad list.

There was a short service in the chapel and then they escorted your father's body, carried in a horse-drawn hearse, to the graveside. There, as the birds sang in the trees and the sun-lit clouds billowed in the sky, your father's coffin was lowered into the ground. Your mother went through it all like a sleepwalker. Her mind was far away, I think, remembering other summer days.

After the funeral, your mother returned with us to Philadelphia and settled back into her room on the fourth floor of the Walnut Street house. She told us that when she woke up in the morning her first thought was that your father was beside her and she was about to tell him of the horrible dream she had just had, and then the empty bed would make her realize that it was no dream but cruel fact. Morning after morning this went on. Sometimes she would dream that there had been a terrible mix-up and he had had to go away but would soon be back. She became confused during her waking hours as well, saying they must be a dream and that she would soon wake up to find your father beside her. And all the time she said how lonely she was.

A week passed and then another and there was no awakening. But then came an awakening of another sort. Early in June she discovered she was with child. At first disbelief, then confirmation and great joy — almost a feeling of relief swept over her. Your father had not totally abandoned her after all. He had returned to her in this miraculous way! He was there inside her and she had a purpose in living, a purpose she could still share with him. A precious part of him, a small substitute was still with her. She wasn't so lonely anymore.

In July Minnie took her to Northeast Harbor on Mt. Desert Island, and she was glad to get back to the cool, quiet Maine seacoast where she and your father had been so happy, but she couldn't bring herself to go to either York or Islesboro. There were too many memories there. Northeast Harbor was safer. She took long walks with her brother Charlie, who gave up his summer plans to go to Europe so he could be with her. She talked incessantly with her mother and any other female that she could find about her coming child.

The weather that summer had reverted to the more typical Maine style of foggy mornings and hazy, sunny afternoons. Somehow this more sober atmosphere was more restful, less demanding, less reminding of her days in Maine with your father than whole days of bright sunshine would have been.

They returned to Philadelphia in September and your mother grew larger with her pregnancy. I had been away for the summer, but joined them in early October, and we spent a quiet fall alternating between town and the family farm near Morestein. She was radiantly healthy the whole time and when in the country would walk around the farm or take long buggy rides over roads carefully chosen for their smoothness to view the fall foliage. In town, she shopped incessantly for her baby.

She had plenty of company to divert her. Friends would drop in at the Walnut Street house for tea or take her for a drive around town and all this kept her quite cheery. But your father's picture was beside her bed, and she said that every night when she lay down she would have a moment where she would reach out to him in her mind before she slept.

Christmas was a quiet affair. Brother Charlie was home from Princeton for the holidays, full of exuberance and college stories. Ma and Ella and I were there and, of course, all the many Philadelphia Whelens were at the Christmas lunch. There was a feeling of solidity in their affection for her and for each other that I am sure was a great comfort to her. New Year's eve came and went, and her time drew near.

Late Thursday night, January 21, 1904, in the same bedroom on the third floor at 2017 Walnut Street, Philadelphia, where she herself had been born, your mother went into labor. It was fairly long, but there were no complications and at two-thirty P.M. the next day, the baby's head was just presenting itself when suddenly and unexpectedly, during the last moments of the delivery, your mother died of a massive heart failure.

There was a brief effort to revive her, but it was obviously futile, and all efforts were turned to save the baby that was you. This was quickly accomplished, and you were set to one side. It was hard for even the doctor to believe that your mother was gone. All during her delivery she had been cheerful and talkative, joking about herself, wondering about the sex of her child. Her contractions came and went with perfect regularity, and there had been no hint of trouble before that terrible spasm contorted her and almost instantly left her limp and dead.

Minnie left the room. There was no joy in her perfectly formed grandson that the nurse was bathing. No joy anywhere. As if seeking to find Violett there, she fled up the stairs to her daughter's room and ran through its emptiness to the window, but she saw nothing beyond it — not the bright blue January sky nor the glistening snow on the brick sidewalks below.

Blindly she stood there and prayed. Not the formal prayer that she was so used to offering up before — all the rote and rituals of the church were shed like clothing, and she stood as if naked before her God. Just a woman begging God directly to rescind that awful moment, to give her but a little forewarning that she might try to avert that terrible second when your mother passed from life to death. She would make any sacrifice He asked to have her back.

Charlie and I entered the room and, coming up behind her, he put his hands on her shoulders to turn her to him, but she was rigid, still locked in her prayer, waiting for an answer. Then Charlie leaned forward, put his head beside hers and pressed his cheek to hers. She gave her first great sob and turned into his arms.

Your grandfather and grandmother Greenough with Ethel, Charles, and Eugenia came from Boston for the funeral, and young Charlie Whelen came up from Princeton, shaken to the core by the sudden loss of his sister. The Greenough and Whelen families and friends assembled in the church on Rittenhouse Square where, only last April, they had witnessed your father and mother's marriage and now heard the same minister that had married them read the burial service over your mother's body.

And so on a cold, rainy Monday afternoon in January 1904, scarcely ten months after her marriage day, your mother was buried in the Whelen family plot at the West Laurel Hill Cemetery outside of Philadelphia, on a hillside overlooking the gray expanse of the Schuylkill River. Young Charlie Whelen refused to leave the graveside after the service, asking to be allowed to remain awhile alone with his sister, so we left him a carriage and departed. It was folly, of course, because it was bitterly cold and wet, but we were not thinking too clearly at the time. As we later learned, he stood there for over an hour in the rain before the driver persuaded him to return to the city.

The death notices were very vivid and some day you should read them I suppose, but they are awfully flowery and sentimental so I don't think I will include them here. There is enough grief to recite as it is.

Then we were dealt another bitter, bitter blow. Less than two weeks after your mother's death, Charlie Whelen, Jr. came down with pneumonia, brought on by the soaking he got at the burial, and died late Saturday night, February 6, 1904, in the Princeton infirmary. He was just twenty years old.

We were all totally destroyed. Both of Minnie and Charlie's children were gone, almost at the same moment. It was too much for them to bear. What had they done to deserve such punishment?

Minnie got the bad news from Charlie, who had been told by his brother Henry. Princeton had called Henry rather than break the news to the Whelens by telegram or by telephone.

It was Sunday morning and we were up and dressed, ready to go to church, when the front doorbell rang and Henry was announced. He asked for a word in private with Charlie and, while Minnie and I waited in the living room, Henry took Charlie downstairs to the small reception room off the front hall where he told him gently what had happened and held him for a moment. Then Henry left him alone to compose himself and walked through to the kitchen where he found the cook and brought two kitchen tumblers of cooking brandy back to where Charlie was dazedly waiting for him. Making him drink one and taking part of the other himself, he helped Charlie up the staircase to the living room.

Overcome with his own grief, Henry sat on the top step of the stairs with the tumbler of brandy dangling in his limp hand while he listened to the murmur of Charlie's voice telling Minnie that their son was also dead. He rose shakily to go to them when her wailing cries told him that she knew.

This time there was no prayer for a reprieve. This time she came close to cursing God for His cruelty. Henry's tumbler of brandy was knocked from his hand and the two men had all they could do to restrain her. She thrashed in their arms as though in physical torture. Finally she went limp and subsided into a state of torpor that was almost more frightening. Her mouth went slack and her eyes glazed over. We thought she had had a stroke, but gradually she regained her composure, and in a husky voice relieved our fears. Henry left her with Charlie and me and ran hatless down the street to the church, where he found the family doctor and brought him back to the house. A strong dose of laudanum was administered and Minnie slept for the next fourteen hours. By then, the whole city knew the story.

It is hard to describe the depth of Minnie's sorrow. She had done almost everything she wanted to accomplish in life, but her future was based on her children and thoughts of grandparenthood. Her husband Charlie and she cared for each other just as fondly as ever, but they had grown apart in the sense that, aside from their children, they had few common interests. Charlie had become submerged in his many business affairs, while she had the children and her music. And now those children were both gone.

A few weeks later, the Whelens came at last to you and suddenly all their love for their lost children went out to this little grandson. Minnie hugged you to her in a frenzy of love and sorrow. Someone took a picture of Minnie holding you, and her face shows the physical ravishment of her sorrow. By strange coincidence, it is exactly the same pose and the same way that she held your mother in a picture taken almost twenty-three years earlier, only in the later picture it is grief, not love, that dominates her face.

The Whelens asked permission from your grandfather Greenough to raise you and to have you named Malcolm Whelen Greenough. Your grandfather consented, and you were so baptized by the Reverend Mr. Tompkins.

The Whelens were not yet ready to assume the active role of caring for their grandson, so you were taken in by Marie Lemoine Harrison, one of your mother's closest friends and a recent mother herself. Minnie and Charlie went to Nestledown for a month's rest.

And so the brief lives of your mother and father came to an end, and we all went back to living our own lives as best we could. Your great uncle, Professor Barrett Wendell,* wrote a letter that sums it all up quite poetically. He was writing from his home in Boston to his son-in-law's

* *Author's note:* Married to Malcolm Scollay Greenough's sister Edith.

father in England on the occasion of the birth of the young couple's first child:

January 24, 1904

Dear Sir Robert:

I have been delaying answer to your last letter until I might send you good news of Mary [Barrett Wendell's daughter]. She was confined, with no sort of mishap, on Friday morning, and her son, to my eye indistinguishable from any other baby, is pronounced by his grandmother as an unusually satisfactory person for his age.

A most poignant sorrow in our family makes us feel all the more how singularly fortunate we are in this personal happiness. While we were in Broomford visiting you, you may remember we received a telegram announcing the death of my wife Edith's nephew, Malcolm Scollay Greenough, Jr., who had been married just one month before. It was only after his death that his poor young wife, Violett, found that she was to have a child. This fact proved to her a deep joy. All through the ensuing months she felt, with a strange kind of exultation, that the coming of this new life kept her still close to her husband, with whom she was passionately in love.

A few hours after Mary's confinement, on the same day, Violett's time came. She had been wonderfully well, up to the last moment. Then, during the actual confinement, something went wrong, and she died almost instantly, without recovering consciousness at all. The child, a boy, was alive and seems strong. Yet I have never known, I think, any more pathetic beginning of a life than is come to the poor little fellow, literally an orphan before he came into the world, his very being bought at the cost of both parents' lives.

His father was a youth of wonderful sweetness, pure as a girl and very far from robust, but the sort that one not only cared for, but respected too. The mother was remarkably beautiful, the picture of spirited vigor, a girl who had had much attention and far more brilliant opportunities than that which she chose. What she idolized in her husband seemed to be his more-than-common simplicity and purity of heart. The memory of them both will be very tender.

The whole story, indeed, has deep beauty, as well as pathos. In this world where so much is sordid, these two young natures lived and loved with utterly stainless passion. To both of them, fortunately, the end came without the agony of any conscious parting from life.

And during the months of her waiting, she was comforted through every hour by the feeling that, for the while, her whole existence was blessedly consecrated to her husband's memory. Had she lived, she must soon have descended again to the everyday realities which would have inevitably poured upon her, and have made the years to come years that would have made the memory of him a thing more and more of the past. For them both, I incline to think, life has proved a great, poetic, single thing. But for the parents of them both, and for the little child they have left behind, there is no consolation for the while. Only years can bring that.

So the joy that has come to us is sobered by the sorrow which struggles with it all the time . . .

Barrett Wendell

Mally, this has exhausted me; I can't write any more for a while. I'll start again in a week or so. — *Aunt Lily*

Malcolm W. Greenough
89 Marlborough Street
Boston, Mass.

March 4, 1926

Dear Aunt Lily,

I can understand how writing that last chapter could be an exhausting emotional experience, so please take some time off before you start up again. I don't want you to make yourself ill.

I have one question, though, that has been bothering me for a long, long time. When I was very little, I had the idea that I had somehow killed both my parents by being born. When I was about fourteen, Aunt Peggy pointed out that I could hardly have killed my father because he died many months before my birth. She said that all women gladly ran the risk of dying in childbirth so I shouldn't feel guilty about that, but I still, even to this day, don't know precisely what caused my mother's death.

You say that she died of heart failure, but was the effort of my birth the cause of her heart failure? Or was "heart failure" just a catch-all phrase they used when they didn't really know what happened?

I don't want to offend your sensibilities or embarrass you, but I really want to know whether it was an abnormality in the birth or just that the birth triggered some existing problem. I know it's probably morbid of me to want to know these details, and I can't explain why they are so important to me but they are. If you can shed any more light on the mystery of why a healthy, robust young woman like my mother should die so suddenly like that please tell me. I've never had the nerve to ask before.

I guess the subject is particularly on my mind now because of Kathleen's pregnancy, especially since she is nowhere near as strong as my mother was.

Thank you for being the kind of person I can talk to about this very private subject.

Much love,
Mally

Author's note: If Aunt Lily ever answered Mally's question, it was in person, for there is no written reply.

Chapter 20

It's been three weeks now since I wrote the last paragraph and I guess I'm ready to go on, but I wish I was done, because I have no idea what writing this chapter is going to produce or what effect it will have on me. It is very strange that even though I think I know what I intend to write, invariably my pen, like a spade with a will of its own, digs up memories that have been long buried and forgotten. Sometimes these are very pleasing to rediscover, and sometimes they are almost more painful than I can bear. But I have started on this course and I will not turn aside now. There are more pleasant subjects to tell of afterwards.

The six years from 1904 to 1910 were a nightmare for the Whelens and the Violetts.

To begin with, Ella died in New Orleans a month after your uncle Charlie Whelen died at Princeton.

Ma, Ella and I had returned to New Orleans right after Charlie's funeral. Ella had been subjected to periods of great despondency for a number of years and her attacks had become more frequent and severe, but her reaction to Violett's and Charlie's deaths was extremely bad — in its own way even worse than Minnie's. Ella's life had always been very ordered and tidy. She hated change of any kind and had great difficulty adapting to it. She just couldn't cope with these two tragedies. She developed a severe tic under her eye, and almost every night she had terrible nightmares that left her soaked in perspiration and shrieking in terror. Besides that she would not or could not eat and the poor thing was wasting away before our eyes.

Our personal physician could do nothing for her except to drug her. He recommended that we try placing her in a hospital called "Le Bon

Dieu," run by the Catholic sisters that specialized in elderly patients. Her condition was worsening at such a rapid rate that we finally agreed. Poor Ella did not want to go, but she didn't have the strength to resist.

The last I saw of her she was lying quietly and apparently peacefully on a narrow bed in a small, whitewashed room with a crucifix on one wall as its only decoration. The next day we were informed by the distraught abbess that Ella had thrown herself out the window and died from the fall to the stone-paved courtyard below.

Poor Ella! She always had such marvelous self control and seemed to rise above all her adversities, but she was very rigid and had to make the world conform to her pattern. Even when she was a little child you had to play the game the way she said it was supposed to be played, and you could never change the rules.

When she was middle-aged she took up bridge and if she thought her partner had played a hand poorly it might upset her so that she couldn't continue. I think she saw some such disorder on a larger scale in Violett's and young Charlie's deaths that so irreparably broke the order of her life that she could find no way to adapt herself or to rearrange the remaining pieces into an acceptable pattern.

Minnie adapted by throwing herself into religion and good works, aided in both by a Miss Addie Dupree, a woman who had, at an earlier time, insinuated herself into the bosom of the Whelen family by her obsequious adoration of Minnie and her willingness to admit that she was a specially favored handmaiden of the Lord, who often heard Him speak. Minnie used to just tolerate her, but after Malcolm's death she was given greater attention, and after Minnie's children died she became sacrosanct. I found her impossible to bear and avoided her at all times, but she was in a position of great power with Minnie, who would allow no one to contradict the now infallible Addie Dupree.

Regrettably, Charlie found protection from these tragedies in retreat. He had always been a quiet man with few original ideas, but now it was as if he had sealed off the borders of his mind to any form of communication whatsoever except those of a business nature. Or perhaps, like the Dutch when invaded, he flooded the lands of his mind to deny access to the enemy.

How did I cope? Well, I had had more practice than the rest in personal devastation even though of a lesser degree, and I had a better eye to survey the wreckage and find the pieces of reusable timber. And you, dear Mally, were the cornerstone of my newest foundation.

David Humphreys' philosophy about life and death, which I have adopted as my own, helped a lot too. I will explain it to you as briefly as possible because it might help you someday.

If there is a heaven and a hell they are right here on earth, not tucked away in some hidden corner of the universe, and you don't gain admission to the former or commitment to the latter because you are a member of any organized religion.

Everyone has a soul, but each new body born doesn't get a new one, nor is the soul consigned at death to a useless semi-existence in heaven or hell along with billions of other bodyless souls — as is implied by the one body equals one soul theory that most Christian faiths profess.

Nor is there such a thing as reincarnation in the sense of dying and returning to life with full memory of one's previous existence. Such a state would be as intolerable as living forever. Even in an eternally healthy body, to live forever would be to experience the same events over and over again, knowing in advance just what was going to happen, being totally bored because there would be nothing new to experience.

In David's view, death is God's way of cleansing the soul of all memory and sending it fresh into the world to experience all its wonders and pains anew. To be a child again, with a child's total confidence in a bright future, is the greatest gift that He has given mankind. Every time someone dies, a baby is born somewhere else, and he or she looks around and says, "Here I am, I wonder what's going to happen next?"

A few weeks after Ella's death Ma and I came back to Philadelphia, and the first thing that I did was to go around to your mother's friend Marie Harrison and bring you back to Minnie's home. Everything had been arranged there before you were born, the nurses, the clothes, the "baby furniture," and all, so it was easy to get you installed — it just needed doing.

The moment you were there, you became the heartbeat of the whole house and slowly we all began to move in a new direction, one that was to give us stability and purpose. You didn't know that you rescued us all, did you?

Minnie began to write two books of children's stories, one that she finished called "Romances in Fanland, or Stories told to Violett" and another companion piece never completed, that was to be called "The Bird and the Sphinx, or Stories told to Malcolm."

When you were just a year old in 1905, they sold the house at 2017 Walnut Street and moved up the street to a new house at 2133. There were too many memories of their children in every nook and cranny of the old house. The move helped to keep the memories at bay, but Minnie said that she felt as though she had been cast adrift on strange seas. She would wake up in the night completely disoriented, or she would be out for a walk and automatically turn in at the old doorway.

Then, in 1907, things took a terrible downturn. Charlie's brothers Henry and Alfred, died within five months of each other, and Minnie suffered a severe hearing loss caused by a bad ear infection. Her hearing became so poor that if there was more than one conversation in the room she couldn't make out what you were saying. All music except a solo piano was lost to her.

From that time on, she and Charlie saw no one but the family and the closest friends. It didn't seem to make much difference to Charlie, but to Minnie, wonderfully entertaining, crowd-loving, music-loving Minnie, it was like solitary confinement. She began to read the Bible constantly and to brood on your dead mother and uncle. Her pretty round face grew loose and lined beyond her years; even her voice lost its rich throaty timbre and became high and querulous. It broke my heart to see her so.

In June of 1908 Ma died. She was eighty-three years old and, as she said so many times that last year, she was ready to go. We were in Atlantic City at the time to get away from the city heat, living in a small, clean hotel just off the boardwalk, with the sound of the waves coming to our windows on the cool Atlantic breezes. I went in to look at her while she was napping one afternoon and she was gone. The expression on her face was almost childish, as though death had wiped the years away.

We took her back home to New Orleans, and on a peaceful summer afternoon Ned, Atwood and I saw her safely into the family vault in the Lafayette Cemetery, just two blocks from our old home (that sadly we no longer owned) on Prytania Street. After the others left we stayed behind for a while. The tablet on the door of our little "house" in the cemetery was getting rather full. There would be just room for one more inscription on the bottom, the last to go would have to use the area up high, just below the pediment, and then that would be "finis" for the Violetts of New Orleans. I thought that it would certainly be Ned who would be the final survivor. He was the youngest, after all, and seemed in excellent health. How could I have guessed then that only eleven years later, on a cold winter evening, he would set fire to his bathrobe while leaning over the fireplace to light his cigarette, and die in horrible agony from his burns.

Losing him almost drove me mad.

Shortly after Ma's death both Minnie and Charlie began to become ill with increasing frequency. It seemed that they only had to hear of a disease to catch it, and gradually the level of their general health spiraled down and down until each new illness became a critical one, each recovery slower and less complete. Finally, in June of 1910, Charlie died, and then ten days later, too sick to be told of his death and burial, Minnie herself succumbed.

I truly believe that your Whelen grandparents, especially Minnie, died of what they used to call "a broken heart." Then too, Minnie and Charlie were victims of the powerful combination of social and religious dogmas prevalent at the time that proclaimed that if you believed in God and the United States of America, loved your family and worked hard, no great harm could befall you.

Until the death of their children your grandparents seemed to be living proof of the validity of that theory. Rich, healthy, regular church-goers and philanthropic, with beautiful, intelligent, well-reared children, there could be nothing but the brightest future ahead of them.

Then, in an instant it was all gone. Not even their worst nightmares could have painted such bleak desolation. God, as Minnie understood Him, had failed to keep his part of the bargain. But that was unthink-able because God was infallible, so therefore she must have somehow failed or "sinned," and this was her punishment. What was her sin? That was her constant question, the puzzle that she could neither solve nor abandon, and in a literal sense, it worried her to death.

I tried so hard to turn her away from that useless, destructive search for non-existent guilt, but she would have none of it. "You are attacking the church," she said, "the one thing that gives me hope!" and in that conviction she was so firmly entrenched and constantly supported by the "sanctified presence" of Miss Dupree that I got nowhere and finally stopped trying. All my efforts only alienated Minnie, and that I could not bear.

You were just five years old when your Whelen grandparents died in June of 1910. Because they had been so ill during their last few months, you had been moved over to the Harrisons again, so I don't know how much you know or remember about it all. I was in Memphis with a friend at the time, and I came on as soon as I got the telegram. I remember so well the moment we arrived at the house and I saw you standing there with Marie Harrison holding your hand. You looked so lost and confused. You saw me, and without a word broke loose and hugged me so hard around the legs that you almost knocked me down.

We had a short funeral service for Minnie, not because of any disrespect for her, but simply because we were all too emotionally drained to endure more. Only Townsend Whelen, his wife Sarah, Atwood and his wife Olga, and I went to the cemetery. As I stood there watching them lower my little sister into the ground next to her husband's grave, with their two dead children lying at their feet, I escaped for a moment into the past, back to one of those dusty, early summer afternoons when we were children playing on the shady balcony of the house on Prytania Street in New Orleans. I was five and Minnie was a toddler of two and the whole unknown world was waiting for us. I woke with a start as Mr. Tompkins finished the service. Here we were in Philadelphia fifty-one years later; Minnie's life had run its course, and you were the sole survivor.

As you know, when your mother died, the Whelens asked your grandfather Greenough if they could raise you, since they had lost both their children, and he had assented. Now he wrote that he would come to take you back with him to Boston. You looked so forlorn those days I couldn't bear it; you were like some little waif in a Dickens novel being taken off to the orphanage. I asked your grandfather if I could accompany you to your new home, and he wrote back to say that he thought it would be a good idea for you to have someone from your mother's family with you in Boston for a while.

So in that dismal summer of 1910, we sadly packed all your parents' unused wedding presents into crates along with most of the better furnishings of Charlie and Minnie's houses in Philadelphia and

Morestein, and put everything into storage against the day that you would reclaim them.

In late July, your grandfather Greenough came down to Philadelphia, and, after a few formalities with the Whelen lawyers, we left. When the train pulled into the Back Bay Station in Boston, it was nine-thirty at night and we had to wake you, and even then you slept through the cab ride to your new home at 7 Gloucester Street. When you woke up the next morning, you had no idea where you were and were very upset, but your cries brought your grandmother and me, and we took you downstairs to become acquainted with your new world.

It was a fine summer day, and after breakfast we all went down Gloucester Street to the Charles River for a walk along the new "embankment," a cement pathway between a grassy bank and huge rectangular granite blocks against which the dark blue waters of the river lapped noisily. A green wrought iron fence ran along the edge of these blocks, and you put your feet between the palings on the lower rung and hoisted yourself up to look down into the moving water. You were fascinated by the bits of flotsam floating by and by the occasional golden carp that revealed itself at the river's edge. "Goldfish!" you cried.

After lunch we showed you another wonder — the Boston Public Garden. We went down Commonwealth Avenue shaded by its continuous line of elms and entered through the Arlington Street gate. You looked up in awe at the towering statue of General Washington sitting on his proud horse with drawn sword in hand, looking off at some unseen enemy. Then we crossed the miniature suspension bridge that bisects the narrow waist of the duck pond and stopped in the middle to watch a swan boat glide underneath. We went down the stairs on the other side and passed under the bridge so that you could experience for the first time the strange effects of light and sound and smell that so impress every child that passes through that cavernous echoing arch. Do you remember any of this?

When you went to sleep that night, I think your mind was so filled with these recent experiences that the past was for the moment forgotten; in fact, from that time on it was as if there was a wall between you and your life in Philadelphia. I don't remember when you next made any reference to Philadelphia — you seemed only to look ahead.

Boston was a totally new environment for you, both in a physical sense and in a family sense. You barely knew your Greenough grandparents and even less your Greenough uncles and aunts. Your aunt Eugenia, who was then twenty-three, was about to be married to Royal Elisha Robbins, Jr., and Ethel, who was thirty, had married Massey Holmes and was living in Kansas City, Missouri. Your uncle Charlie Greenough had married Margaret Perkins and lived in Brookline, Massachusetts. They were all very kind to you and did their best to make you feel at home, and for a while all went well. You were enrolled in the local school and life seemed to have settled down to a peaceful, secure routine. You made friends easily among the other children your age in the Back Bay and in Nahant, where your grandparents still had their summer house that they had purchased back in the 1870's.

Then in February of 1911, your grandmother Lizzie Tiffany Greenough died. She had not been very well, but neither had she had any specific illness. She just went to bed early one night, and in the morning her maid found her dead. Her death left your grandfather a widower with no desire to remarry or otherwise provide a female to help to raise his grandson in his own home. He tried it alone for two years and then concluded that you would be better off in a boarding school and enrolled you at the Fay School in Southboro, Massachusetts.

So in September 1913, at the great age of nine, you entered the boarding school world. What your thoughts were at the time can only be guessed at, but certainly you must have been a very lonely, insecure little boy, once more removed to a totally new life.

I won't go into a history of your life since then, but I do want to tell you how proud I am of all the prizes for scholarship and medals for athletics and the great number of friends that you began to accumulate then. You certainly didn't waste your time brooding over your problems. I'll never forget how thrilled I was when I heard that in your very first school year you were ranked first in your form for every month of each term, and between third and fifteenth in the whole school. And that was carrying eight courses!

Your ability to make new friends was amazing and very reassuring after all that had happened to you. You were beginning to build a bank account of friends for insurance against the awful feelings of loss and loneliness that you had known before.

Your letters to me then were full of stories about your adventures in school and, particularly, in Nahant. Names like Cabot Lodge, Jimmy Bangs, Gray Otis, Willy Beal, and Alf Codman appeared constantly. Your tales of roaming the coast in your eighteen-foot dory with these boys scared me because I was sure you would be swept out to sea by a sudden storm and drowned.

Remember when I came up to Groton to see you play in the St. Marks football game your sixth form year? You were a good player I am sure, but the game was so rough and so many other boys got hurt I was a wreck before it was over. And you were so charming and gallant at tea later at the headmaster's house. You made your old Aunt Lily feel like your "date" the way you took me around the room and presented me not only to the masters, but also to your team-mates. You all looked so scrubbed clean and well groomed that it was hard to believe that you were those same mud-covered figures that had run off the field an hour earlier.

Taking about "dates" (I love that expression), I have a special place in my heart for the time you came down to New York when I was staying with Atwood and Olga. You were sixteen and were going to a dance with your Groton friend Johnny Pratt, but the next day you came to call and took me out to lunch at the Plaza. That was a lovely afternoon.

Of course, there were many times we saw each other over the years; I made certain that there would be, but these ones that I am describing are the special ones that stand out in my mind, and I just want you to know how much they meant to me.

Oh, there was one other. Do you remember the summer of 1921 when I spent a month with you and your grandfather in Marblehead? How could I have forgotten to mention that? It was the second time I ever went sailing in my whole life. I was scared to death when I got into that launch at the Eastern Yacht Club and committed myself to an afternoon on the water in that tippy-looking little sailboat. I remember you saying, "Aunt Lily, it's a big sailboat, it's thirty-six feet long, and it can't tip over. It's got a big keel with lead at the bottom. Grandpa and I are good sailors. Don't worry, you'll have a swell time!"

Well, you were right, I did have a "swell" time, but I was very relieved to get back on dry land.

I'm sorry I missed your Harvard graduation, especially since you were the President of your class and the Class Marshall and the Captain of the football team and all those other honors. It was so frustrating to be sick — really sick — at that particular time, about the only time I can remember being so sick since I was a little girl in Toronto after the war. I did so want to be there and shine in your reflected glory, just as I did at your father's graduation from Law School back in 1902.

Well, I guess I've finally come to the end of my story, and I can see from reading these last few pages that my "book" has turned back into a letter to you. I guess the whole thing is really just that, one long letter to my grandnephew who I love like my own grandson. I'm sorry that there is so much in it about me — I just got carried away reliving those times. I hope that doesn't spoil it for you. Since, as I said above, I seem to have reverted to letter style, I'll end by saying,

> With all my love from your devoted
> *Aunt Lily*
>> May 11, 1926

Chapter 21

ST. CHARLES HOTEL
3915 St. Charles Street
New Orleans, La.

September 23, 1926

Dear Mally,

The most utterly incredible thing has happened! You just won't believe it! It's been a week now and I still don't believe it myself. William is here in New Orleans! William Robertson! MY William!

Last Tuesday afternoon, I was in my room getting ready to go down to the tea the management serves in the reading room off the lobby when the boy came up and told me that there were two gentlemen downstairs asking to see me. As I came down the staircase, I noticed them immediately because they were the only strangers there.

One was an older man, in his early seventies I judged, and the other about thirty years his junior. Both were handsome, elegantly dressed and strangely alike. There was something puzzlingly familiar about them both. But who could they be?

As I approached, the older gentleman came to meet me, and we stopped a few feet from each other. I still didn't know who it was. "Lily, it's me . . . William . . . ," he said, and the sound of his voice told me what I had failed to see.

I stood there for a moment surrounded by a mist of emotion that separated me from the rest of the world while this incredible event sunk in. It was one of those moments that seems so long and yet is only an instant, and then I came forward to take his hands in mine and stupidly

225

say "William," and he as inanely repeated "Lily." Then there was a truly long pause because I didn't know where to begin. Who would after all those years?

William gave us some recovery time by introducing his companion. "Lily," he said, "this is my son, Arthur. Arthur, this is the lady I have told you so much about, Miss Lily Violett."

Gradually, over many cups of tea, I got the story. William's wife died in 1921 after almost fifteen years of illness and mental disturbances. Their children had long since settled into careers and marriages and had children of their own. Arthur had become a banker like his father, married rather late in life and had one child, a boy named Langdon. Arthur was a much more successful banker than his father and came to the attention of the representative of a large bank in St. Louis that was looking for someone to head up their European office. The pay offered was stupendous compared to what he was getting and the opportunities seemed very good, so he accepted their offer, subject to his being confirmed to the position after a personal interview in St. Louis.

Since there was nothing in particular keeping William in England, he decided to accompany his son on the trip, and when the travel agent suggested that the trip could be routed through New Orleans as easily as New York, they decided to come this way.

William said that he had no idea what he would find when we met and how pleased he was to find me so much the way he remembered me. We are, after all, both in our seventies, but if I do say so myself we are a pretty well-preserved old pair. William's hair is as snowy white as mine, as is his long mustache, and his face is lined and weathered, but his smile and his eyes are just the same and that wonderful voice that I have remembered when other features faded is still as strong and resonant as ever.

I asked him how he found me, and he replied that I seemed a bit plumper, but he thought it most becoming. He said that he was particularly glad that I had not succumbed to modern fashions but had left my hair long. As a girl, when we first met, I wore it loose, and he said he thought that if I would unbraid it now it would fall almost to my waist as it did then. The idea made me blush scarlet, something I haven't done in years.

William has decided to remain here while Arthur goes to St. Louis about his new job so that, as he puts it, we can get "better acquainted." I am as excited by the prospect as a schoolgirl.

I will write again soon. My love to you all and especially to your new son, Malcolm Whelen Greenough, Jr. I am so glad you are continuing the use of the Whelen name. Minnie and Charlie would be very happy about that.

Your affectionate and very happy
Aunt Lily

Postscript

My Aunt Lily Violett became Mrs. William Robertson on October 21, 1926. I attended the wedding alone because Kathleen didn't feel she could leave little Mally, Jr., then only four months old. I would have liked to have brought him with us, but was vetoed on that proposal.

Aunt Lily and "Uncle" William, as I insisted he be called, may have been elderly on their wedding day, but there was nothing ancient about either one of them. I don't know what Uncle William looked like before, but Aunt Lily looked a good ten years younger and Uncle William stood as straight and strong as any man in the congregation.

As they spoke their vows in church there were tears in my eyes the whole time; in fact, I was a snuffling wreck when it was over. I thought about all those years they were apart and how faithful they had been to their love for each other. In my life many relations have been taken away from me, and this addition of one new "uncle" and one rejuvenated and very happy aunt was a great joy to me.

Aunt Lily and Uncle William were the most loving and loveable couple I have ever known. It was thrilling to me to be in their company and witness their expressions of affection — a pat on the cheek or hand, a brief, hard hug, or the looks they gave each other from time to time when their eyes met were wonderful to behold. There was an intensity about their relationship you could feel, it was so strong.

They bought a small house in New Orleans where they were the center of a fascinating group of friends, but they also traveled widely both in this country and abroad. Their energy was phenomenal — new places and people seemed to provide them with the new inspiration for further adventure. They made new friends everywhere, and of a range of ages that was surprising. Many times in my travels, I have met people of a contemporary age to my own, and on announcing my name, heard the response "Oh, you're Lily Robertson's grandnephew. She's mentioned you so often!"

At least once a year they visited with us in Boston, usually in the late fall on the way home from their annual trip abroad, which always included a stay at the Olneys' manor, now a first-class country inn. They were great walkers and loved the English countryside in the early fall.

Aunt Lily died on May 1, 1937, at the age of eighty-three. She was in excellent health and clear of mind right up until the end. They went to bed one night, and when Uncle William woke up the next morning, he reached over to her and knew she was gone. He died two years later of pneumonia at ninety.

I am so glad that Aunt Lily went first and didn't have to go through the pain of another personal loss, especially one so dear and so long awaited as her William.

Malcolm Whelen Greenough
September 16, 1941

Family Sources

VIOLETT – OLDHAM FAMILY TREE (PARTIAL)

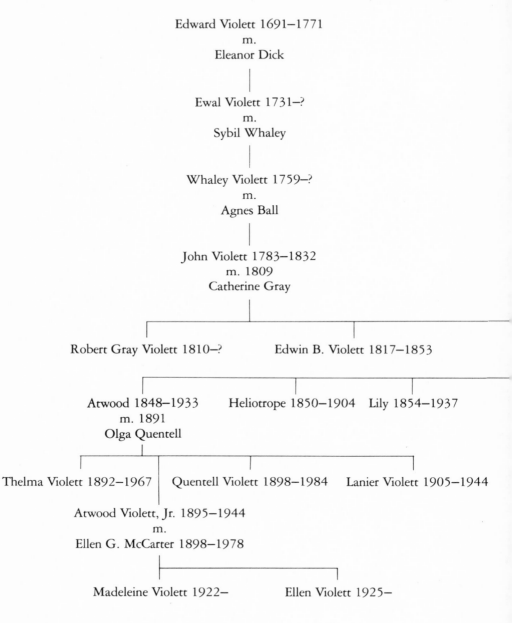

Edward Violett 1691–1771
m.
Eleanor Dick

Ewal Violett 1731–?
m.
Sybil Whaley

Whaley Violett 1759–?
m.
Agnes Ball

John Violett 1783–1832
m. 1809
Catherine Gray

Robert Gray Violett 1810–?   Edwin B. Violett 1817–1853

Atwood 1848–1933   Heliotrope 1850–1904   Lily 1854–1937
m. 1891
Olga Quentell

Thelma Violett 1892–1967 | Quentell Violett 1898–1984   Lanier Violett 1905–1944

Atwood Violett, Jr. 1895–1944
m.
Ellen G. McCarter 1898–1978

Madeleine Violett 1922–   Ellen Violett 1925–

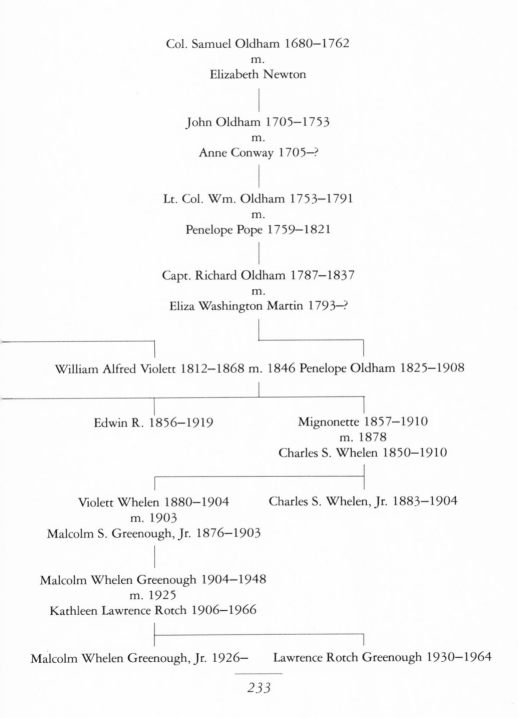

Col. Samuel Oldham 1680–1762
m.
Elizabeth Newton

John Oldham 1705–1753
m.
Anne Conway 1705–?

Lt. Col. Wm. Oldham 1753–1791
m.
Penelope Pope 1759–1821

Capt. Richard Oldham 1787–1837
m.
Eliza Washington Martin 1793–?

William Alfred Violett 1812–1868 m. 1846 Penelope Oldham 1825–1908

Edwin R. 1856–1919   Mignonette 1857–1910
m. 1878
Charles S. Whelen 1850–1910

Violett Whelen 1880–1904   Charles S. Whelen, Jr. 1883–1904
m. 1903
Malcolm S. Greenough, Jr. 1876–1903

Malcolm Whelen Greenough 1904–1948
m. 1925
Kathleen Lawrence Rotch 1906–1966

Malcolm Whelen Greenough, Jr. 1926–   Lawrence Rotch Greenough 1930–1964

233

WHELEN – GREENOUGH FAMILY TREES (PARTIAL)

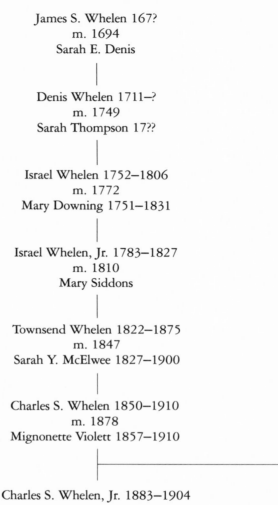

James S. Whelen 167?
m. 1694
Sarah E. Denis

Denis Whelen 1711–?
m. 1749
Sarah Thompson 17??

Israel Whelen 1752–1806
m. 1772
Mary Downing 1751–1831

Israel Whelen, Jr. 1783–1827
m. 1810
Mary Siddons

Townsend Whelen 1822–1875
m. 1847
Sarah Y. McElwee 1827–1900

Charles S. Whelen 1850–1910
m. 1878
Mignonette Violett 1857–1910

Charles S. Whelen, Jr. 1883–1904

John Greenough 1672–1732
m. 1693
Elizabeth Grosse 1673–1746

|

Thomas Greenough 1710–1785
m. 1750
Sarah Stoddard 1718–1778

|

Rev. Wm. Greenough 1756–1831
m. 1785
Abigail Badger 1765–1796

|

William Greenough 1792–1874
m. 1817
Sarah Gardner 1798–1882

|

Wm. W. Greenough 1818–1899
m. 1841
Catherine Scollay Curtis 1821–1899

|

Malcolm S. Greenough 1848–1932
m. 1872
Elizabeth Tiffany 1849–1911

Violett Whelen 1880–1904 m. 1903 Malcolm S. Greenough, Jr. 1876–1903

|

Malcolm Whelen Greenough 1904–1948
m. 1925
Kathleen Lawrence Rotch 1906–1966

Malcolm Whelen Greenough, Jr. 1926–   Lawrence Rotch Greenough 1930–1964

FLOOR PLAN OF
WILLIAM A. VIOLETT HOUSE, NEW ORLEANS

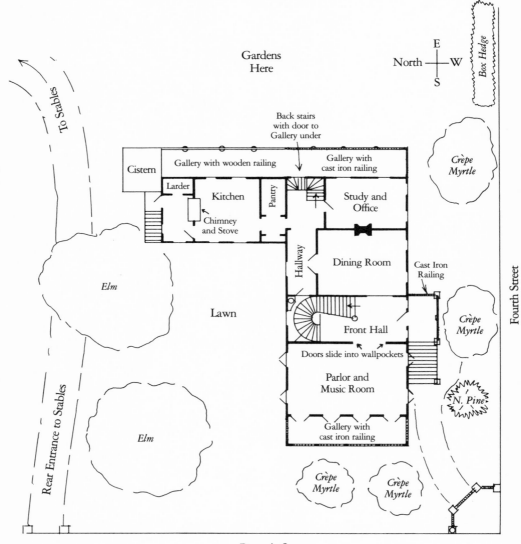

Gardens
Here

North

E
W
S

Box Hedge

To Stables

Back stairs
with door to
Gallery under

Cistern

Gallery with wooden railing

Gallery with
cast iron railing

Crèpe
Myrtle

Larder

Kitchen

Pantry

Study and
Office

Chimney
and Stove

Elm

Hallway

Dining Room

Cast Iron
Railing

Fourth Street

Lawn

Crèpe
Myrtle

Front Hall

Doors slide into wallpockets

N. Pine

Rear Entrance to Stables

Elm

Parlor and
Music Room

Gallery with
cast iron railing

Crèpe
Myrtle

Crèpe
Myrtle

Prytania Street

First Floor

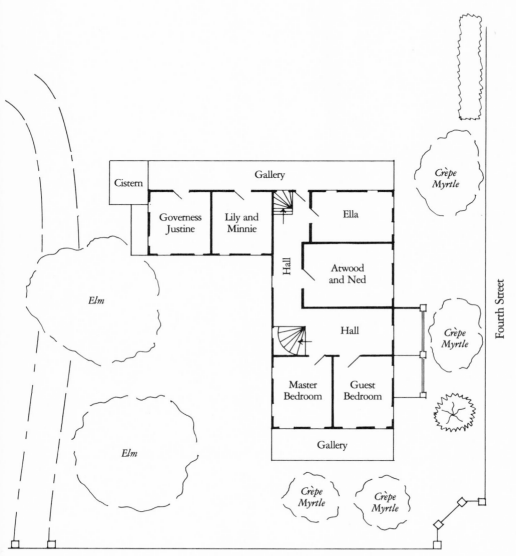

Second Floor

237

LIST OF DOCUMENTS

Diary of Mignonette Violett Whelen 1879–1886.

Diary of Lily Violett 1909–1927.

Diary of Malcolm Scollay Greenough, Jr. 1894–1898.

Letters of Penelope Oldham Violett 1867–1907.

Letters to and from Lily Violett 1919–1926.

Letters, notes and poetry of Mignonette V. Whelen.

Letters of Charles S. Whelen 1898–1903.

Letters of Heliotrope Violett 1898–1903.

Letters of Edwin Violett 1898–1919.

Letters of Addie M.C. Dupree 1902–1904.

Letters of Malcolm Scollay Greenough 1871–1910.

Letters of congratulation on engagement of V.W. & M.S.G. Jr.

Letters of Malcolm Scollay Greenough, Jr. 1885–1903.

Letters of Lizzie Tiffany Greenough 1879–1906.

Letters of Violett Whelen 1889–1904.

Letters and poetry of Atwood Violett 1884–1930.

Letter of May Goetzen to M.V. Whelen, March 2, 1904.

Letter of Barrett Wendell dated 24 January, 1904.

Holographic will of William Alfred Violett dated 1864.

Pass granted to Atwood Violett May 14, 1865 by U.S. Gen. Canby.

Deed of trust by Malcolm Scollay Greenough Feb. 10, 1896.

Book of wedding presents of Violett Whelen–1903.

"Marpessa" by Stephen Phillips, John Lane of London & New York.

"Toinette's Philip" by Mrs. C.V. Jamison, Century Co., 1896.

"Romances of Fanland" by Mignonette Violett Whelen, Philadelphia, Pa.,1906.